Target
Get back on track

1

AQA GCSE (9–1)
Biology

Heidi Foxford, Janette Gledhill

Pearson

Published by Pearson Education Limited, 80 Strand, London, WC2R ORL.

www.pearsonschoolsandfecolleges.co.uk

Text and illustrations © Pearson Education Ltd 2018
Typeset and illustrated by QBS Learning
Produced by QBS Learning

The rights of Heidi Foxford and Janette Gledhill to be identified as authors of this work have been asserted by them in accordance with the Copyright, Designs and Patents Act 1988.

First published 2018

21 20 19 18
10 9 8 7 6 5 4 3 2 1

British Library Cataloguing in Publication Data
A catalogue record for this book is available from the British Library

ISBN 978 1 292 24576 8

Acknowledgements
The authors and publisher would like to thank the following individuals and organisations for their kind permission to reproduce copyright material.

Photographs

(Key: b-bottom; c-centre; l-left; r-right; t-top)

Alamy Stock Photo: Cavallini James/BSIP SA 62; **Shutterstock:** D. Kucharski K. Kucharska 57, 63

All other images © Pearson Education

Note from the publisher
Pearson has robust editorial processes, including answer and fact checks, to ensure the accuracy of the content in this publication, and every effort is made to ensure this publication is free of errors. We are, however, only human, and occasionally errors do occur. Pearson is not liable for any misunderstandings that arise as a result of errors in this publication, but it is our priority to ensure that the content is accurate. If you spot an error, please do contact us at resourcescorrections@pearson.com so we can make sure it is corrected.

 This workbook has been developed using the Pearson Progression Map and Scale for Science.

To find out more about the Progression Scale for Science and to see how it relates to indicative GCSE (9–1) grades go to www.pearsonschools.co.uk/ProgressionServices

Helping you to formulate grade predictions, apply interventions and track progress.

Any reference to indicative grades in the Pearson Target Workbooks and Pearson Progression Services is not to be used as an accurate indicator of how a student will be awarded a grade for their GCSE exams.

You have told us that mapping the Steps from the Pearson Progression Maps to indicative grades will make it simpler for you to accumulate the evidence to formulate your own grade predictions, apply any interventions and track student progress. We're really excited about this work and its potential for helping teachers and students. It is, however, important to understand that this mapping is for guidance only to support teachers' own predictions of progress and is not an accurate predictor of grades.

Our Pearson Progression Scale is criterion referenced. If a student can perform a task or demonstrate a skill, we say they are working at a certain Step according to the criteria. Teachers can mark assessments and issue results with reference to these criteria which do not depend on the wider cohort in any given year. For GCSE exams however, all Awarding Organisations set the grade boundaries with reference to the strength of the cohort in any given year. For more information about how this works please visit: https://www.gov.uk/government/news/setting-standards-for-new-gcses-in-2017

Contents

1 Transport

This unit will help you explain in more detail how diffusion, osmosis and active transport occur. This unit will help you understand the factors that can affect the rate of diffusion.

In the exam, you will be asked to answer questions such as the one below.

Exam-style question

1   A student set up the experiment shown in Figure 1 to investigate osmosis.
    This is the method used.

  1.   Make two tubes of Visking tubing (partially permeable membrane).

  2.   Put $25\,cm^3$ of 20% sucrose solution into tube **A**.

  3.   Put $25\,cm^3$ of pure (distilled) water into tube **B**.

  4.   Put both tubes in 5% sucrose solution and leave for 1 hour.

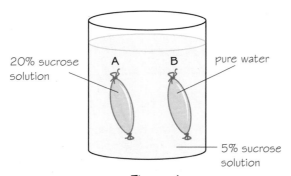

20% sucrose solution

A   B   pure water

5% sucrose solution

Figure 1

After 1 hour, tube **B** looks smaller than before.

Predict the appearance of tube **A**.

Explain your answer.   (4 marks)

You will already have done some work on this topic. Before starting the **skills boosts**, rate your confidence in diffusion, osmosis and active transport. Colour in 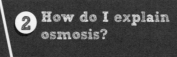 the bars.

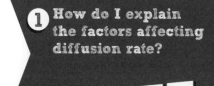

1 How do I explain the factors affecting diffusion rate?

2 How do I explain osmosis?

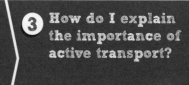

3 How do I explain the importance of active transport?

Diffusion is the spreading out of the particles of any substance in solution, or particles of a gas. It results in the net movement of substances from an area of high concentration to an area of low concentration. It is a **passive process** (it requires no energy).

> **Net** movement describes the overall amount of movement. If equal amounts of molecules move in opposite directions, there is no overall or net movement.

(1) Alveoli in the lungs are where gas exchange occurs in mammals. This is a form of diffusion.

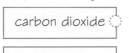 **a** Draw lines to link the gases to the places where they have a higher concentration.

> Carbon dioxide is carried in the blood in red blood cells and in the plasma.

| carbon dioxide | ○---○ | higher concentration in alveolus than in capillary |
| oxygen | ○---○ | higher concentration in capillary than in alveolus |

b Draw an arrow in blue on the diagram to show the direction in which carbon dioxide molecules will move.

c Draw an arrow in red on the diagram to show the direction in which oxygen molecules will move.

Osmosis is a form of diffusion concerned with the movement of water molecules.

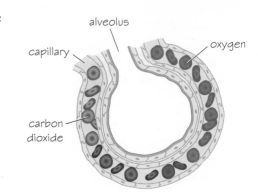

alveolus

capillary

oxygen

carbon dioxide

(2) Write a definition of osmosis using all the words in the box. You can use the words more than once.

> diffusion   partially   permeable   dilute   osmosis
>
> solution   water   membrane   concentrated

....

....

....

(3) The top diagram shows a model of root hair cells in the roots of plants taking up water by osmosis.

a Draw an arrow on the diagram to show the direction in which the water molecules will move.

water molecules in the surrounding soil

root hair cells

Water molecules move from low to high solute concentration.

Active transport is different from diffusion, because it requires **energy**, uses **transport proteins** in the cell membrane and goes **against** a concentration gradient (from low to high).

Root hair cells absorb mineral ions by active transport, as shown in the lower diagram.

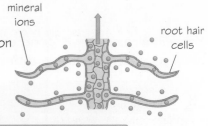

mineral ions

root hair cells

b Draw an arrow on the lower diagram to show the direction in which mineral ions will move.

c Circle the correct words in the sentences below to explain how root hair cells absorb mineral ions.

> Mineral ions are at a **higher / lower** concentration in the soil than inside the plant.
>
> Root hair cells use **water / energy** to move mineral ions **against / towards** the concentration gradient.

How do I explain the factors affecting diffusion rate?

Three factors affect the rate of diffusion. These are the difference in concentration, the temperature and the surface area of the membrane. But it is the amount of surface area available for every unit of volume of an organism that is important to ensure sufficient diffusion to meet the needs of the organism. This is measured as surface area : volume ratio.

Surface area : volume ratio The higher the SA : V ratio, the greater the rate of diffusion.

Rate of diffusion is a measure of the number of randomly moving molecules passing through a surface area per unit time.

① The diagram shows two beakers containing the same volume and concentration of hydrochloric acid. The pink agar blocks contain a mixture of pH indicator and an alkali. As the acid diffuses into an agar block, it neutralises the alkali and turns the block colourless.

Complete ✏️ the table to decide the order in which the blocks will become colourless.

1cm × 1cm × 1cm block of agar

2cm × 2cm × 2cm block of agar

The higher the SA : V ratio, the greater the exposure of the block to the acid.

24 : 8 simplifies to 3 : 1.

6 : 1 is a higher SA : V ratio than 3 : 1.

Block	Surface area in cm²	Volume in cm³	SA : V	Order of colour change
A	6 (1cm × 1cm × 6 sides)	1 (1cm × 1cm × 1cm)	6 : 1	
B				

Concentration gradient The greater the difference between the concentration of substances inside and outside the cell, the greater the concentration gradient and the greater the rate of diffusion.

② Some students measured the rate of diffusion in two agar blocks of the same size. The agar blocks were placed in the same volume of hydrochloric acid at **different** concentrations. Their results are shown below.

Beaker	Hydrochloric acid concentration in g/dm³	Diffusion path (distance to centre of block) in cm	Time taken in minutes	Rate of diffusion in cm/minute
A	35	1	2	
B	70	1	1	

ⓐ Complete ✏️ the table to calculate the rate of diffusion in each beaker.

ⓑ Complete ✏️ these sentences.

A greater concentration means there are more particles to move across compared with a lower concentration so diffusion will be faster.

The agar block in beaker .... turned colourless first. This is because the ....

gradient was .... and the rate of diffusion was the ....

③ Circle Ⓐ the best words to explain how increasing temperature affects the rate of diffusion.

The particles have **more / less** energy so they move around **slower / faster** causing an **increase / decrease** in the rate of diffusion.

Temperature is a measure of the kinetic energy within particles, so hotter particles move faster, causing diffusion to happen more quickly.

② How do I explain osmosis?

Explaining osmosis requires an understanding of solute concentration. A **solute** is a substance dissolved in a solvent such as water. Salt and sugar are common solutes. If a solution has a low solute concentration, then it has a high water concentration. This is called a dilute solution. If a cell contains a lower solute concentration than the solution outside, water molecules will move **out of** the cell into the solution, and the cell will shrink.

① Circle the best words in bold to complete this sentence.

> If a cell contains a much lower solute concentration than in the solution outside, water
>
> molecules will move **into** / **out of** the cell, and the cell will eventually **shrink** / **burst**.

② The diagram shows red blood cells in salt solutions at three different concentrations. Different changes have happened to each red blood cell as a result.

Draw lines to show whether the solute concentration in each beaker is equal to, higher than or lower than the solute concentration of the cell cytoplasm.

| | A | B | C |

solution in beaker **A**   equal to

solution in beaker **B**   higher than

solution in beaker **C**   lower than

Red blood cell breaks up   Red blood cell remains the same size   Red blood cell shrivels

③ Strawberry cells contain water with a low concentration of fruit sugars dissolved in solution. The diagram shows some strawberries with sugar sprinkled on them. After 3 hours, a syrup has formed around the strawberries.

Explain, in terms of osmosis, why this syrup has formed.

after 3 hours

strawberries sprinkled with sugar   strawberries in sugar syrup

....

....

....

....

....

....

What effect does the sprinkled sugar have on the solute concentration outside the strawberry cells?

Remember Water molecules move from a low solute concentration to a higher solute concentration.

④ Three cells of different solute concentrations are placed in a 25 per cent sugar solution, as shown in the diagram.

Draw arrows from each cell to show the **net** direction of water molecule movement between cells and into or out of the solution, based on the solute concentrations shown.

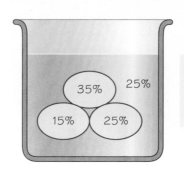

35%   25%

15%   25%

Remember Higher solute concentration = lower water molecule concentration.

③ How do I explain the importance of active transport?

Unlike diffusion and osmosis, **active transport** requires **energy** to move molecules **against** the concentration gradient through special **transport proteins** in cell membranes.

① The diagram shows a root hair cell and mineral ions. Active transport is important to plants in order to get low levels of minerals from the surrounding soil into their root system.

Draw 🖉 lines from the labels to the correct letters (**A–E**) on the diagram to show how active transport works.

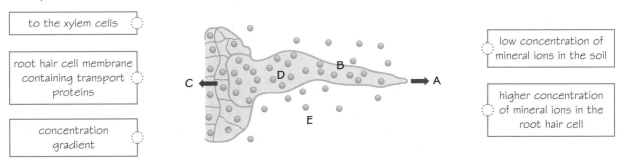

to the xylem cells

root hair cell membrane containing transport proteins

concentration gradient

low concentration of mineral ions in the soil

higher concentration of mineral ions in the root hair cell

② In our bodies, active transport plays an important role in digestion. The diagram shows a model of our digestive system. Sodium ions are shown in yellow.

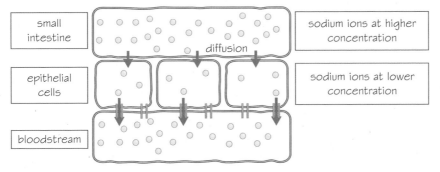

small intestine

epithelial cells

bloodstream

diffusion

sodium ions at higher concentration

sodium ions at lower concentration

a Circle Ⓐ the correct words in bold to complete this student's explanation of how sodium ions move from the small intestine into the blood.

Sodium ions are **less / more** concentrated in the small intestine than in the epithelial cells. They move into the epithelial cells by diffusion. Sodium ions are at a **higher / lower** concentration in the epithelial cells than in the bloodstream, and need to move **against / down** the concentration gradient by **osmosis / active transport**. This requires **transport proteins / cellulose** in the cell membrane and **carbon dioxide / energy** from respiration.

b On the diagram below, draw 🖉 lines to join the labels on the right to the letters **A**, **B** and **C**.

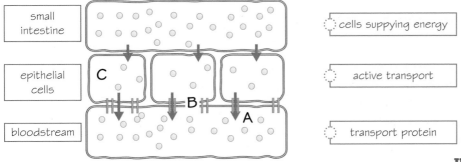

small intestine

epithelial cells

bloodstream

cells suppying energy

active transport

transport protein

Sample response

Your understanding of diffusion, osmosis and active transport will often be tested in the context of a core practical.

Look at this exam-style question and the answers given by a student.

1 A student investigated osmosis in beetroot cubes.
   This is the method used.

   1. Cut beetroot into equal-sized cubes and record the mass of each cube.

   2. Place each cube into a different concentration of salt solution, then remove the cubes after 30 minutes.

   3. Pat the beetroot cubes dry with tissue paper, and record the final mass of each cube.

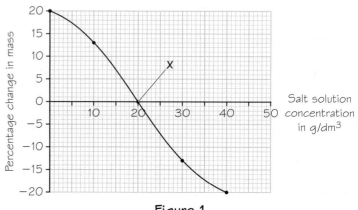

Figure 1

The student's results are shown in Figure 1.

1.1 Give a reason why the outside of the beetroot cube must be dried. **(1 mark)**

   Water that is still on the cube may add to the mass, by drying it the cube may have an accurate mass.

1.2 Explain the conclusion that can be made about point **X** on the graph. **(2 marks)**

   At a concentration of 20 g/dm³, there is no change in the mass of the beetroot.

1.3 Give one way the student could obtain more data to increase the accuracy of point **X**. **(1 mark)**

   Include a larger range of salt solutions.

① **a** Justify ✎ why the student achieved the mark for **1.1**.

   ....

   b The student achieved only 1 mark for **1.2**. How could the student have achieved the other mark? ✎

   ....

   c The student did not achieve the mark for **1.3**. What response would have achieved the mark? ✎

   ....

Your turn!

It is now time to use what you have learned to answer the exam-style question from page 1.
Remember to read the question thoroughly, looking for information that may help you.
Make good use of your knowledge from other areas of biology.

Read the exam-style question and answer it using the hints to guide you.

Exam-style question

1   A student set up the experiment shown in Figure 1 to investigate osmosis.
    This is the method used.

1.   Make two tubes of Visking tubing (a partially permeable membrane).

2.   Put $25\,cm^3$ of 20% sucrose solution into tube **A**.

3.   Put $25\,cm^3$ of pure (distilled) water into tube **B**.

4.   Put both tubes in 5% sucrose solution and leave for 1 hour.

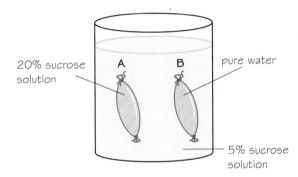

20% sucrose solution

pure water

5% sucrose solution

Figure 1

After 1 hour, tube **B** looks smaller than before.

Predict the appearance of tube **A**.

Explain your answer.

Which process is taking place: diffusion, osmosis or active transport?

'Predict' means say what you think will happen based on what you know.

(4 marks)

There are 4 marks available, so try to identify four different points as answers.

Will tube A have increased in size, decreased in size or stayed the same size? Is there a more accurate way of describing this?

Has the question given you any clues about how the sucrose and water molecules are kept separate?

Think about where the high and low solute concentrations are and how this will influence the movement of substances.

Need more practice?

Questions about transport of substances could occur as part of a question on how the structure of a tissue or organ is related to its function or as stand-alone questions.

Have a go at these exam-style questions. ✎

1 Describe how gases are exchanged through the skin of an earthworm.　　(2 marks)

....

....

....

2 A red blood cell is placed into pure water. The cell bursts. Explain why this happens.　　(3 marks)

....

....

....

....

3 Explain how mineral ions are absorbed by root hair cells in plants.　　(3 marks)

....

....

....

4 Multicelluar organisms need specialised exchange surfaces, such as gills or lungs, to supply oxygen to the cells of the organism. Explain why single-celled organisms do not need specialised exchange structures.　　(2 marks)

....

....

....

Boost your grade

To improve your grade, practise answering questions on the osmosis investigation using different examples. You will use potatoes as the example in the lab. However, exam questions may test your ability to apply your knowledge to another example and explain the results of that experiment.

How confident do you feel about each of these **skills**? Colour in ✎ the bars.

1 How do I explain the factors affecting diffusion rate?

2 How do I explain osmosis?

3 How do I explain the importance of active transport?

② Plant biology

This unit will help you to understand how different factors affect transpiration in plants and how to calculate and interpret data on transpiration. It will also help you to understand how factors that limit photosynthesis interact with each other.

In the exam, you will be asked to answer questions such as the one below.

Exam-style question

1 Figure 1 shows how carbon dioxide concentration affects the rate of photosynthesis in radish plants kept at 16 °C.

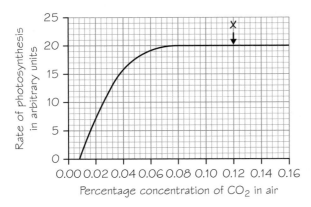

Figure 1

1.1 What is the maximum rate of photosynthesis of the radish plant shown by the graph? **(1 mark)**

1.2 Suggest one factor that could be limiting the rate of photosynthesis at point X. **(1 mark)**

Radish plants grow best at around 16 °C. Above this temperature, radishes are prone to losing too much water through transpiration.

1.3 Explain why higher temperatures cause an increase in transpiration. **(2 marks)**

You will already have done some work on plants. Before starting the **skills boosts**, rate your confidence in these areas of plant biology. Colour in (✐) the bars.

① How do I explain the effect of changing different factors on the rate of transpiration?

② How do I calculate and interpret data on water loss in plants?

③ How do I explain how limiting factors interact?

Transpiration is a vital process that occurs in plants. It is the movement of water from the roots to the leaves. Transpiration explains how water moves up the plant **against gravity** without the use of a pump.

The diagram shows how water moves through a plant in the transpiration stream.

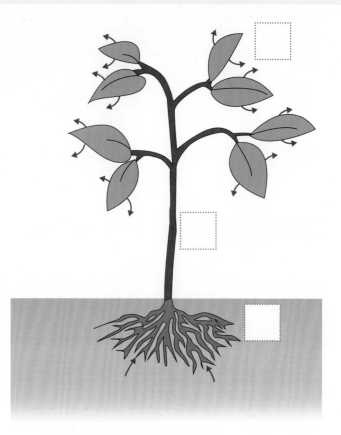

(**1**) Write 🖉 the letters A, B and C in the correct positions on the diagram.

A Water is transported to the leaves through xylem tubes.

B Water vapour escapes out of small pores called stomata.

C Water enters the plant by osmosis in root hair cells.

> Stomata are tiny holes found in the upper and lower surface/epidermis of the leaf.

As plants lose water from their leaves, more water is drawn into the roots. This is because there is a continuous column of water from root to leaf, so water is drawn into the roots as water is lost from the leaf.

This diagram is a cross-section of a leaf showing one of the tiny holes (a stoma) on the surface of the leaf, through which plants lose water.

Water inside the leaf **evaporates** from the surface of the spongy mesophyll cells into the air spaces inside the leaf.

Water vapour inside the air spaces **diffuses** out of the stomata and into the air surrounding the leaf.

spongy mesophyll cells

air space   stoma   guard cell

> **Remember** Evaporation is the process of turning liquid water into water vapour.

(**2**) Draw 🖉 an arrow to show the overall movement of the water vapour out of the leaf.

Different environmental factors affect the rate at which water particles evaporate and diffuse out of the leaf. A factor that speeds up the rate of evaporation and diffusion of water out of the leaf will increase the rate of transpiration in a plant.

(**3**) From the words in the box, circle Ⓐ two factors that would speed up the rate of transpiration in a plant.

> increased temperature   decreased temperature
>
> increased humidity   increased air movement

1 **How do I explain the effect of changing different factors on the rate of transpiration?**

The rate at which water is lost from a plant is affected by four main environmental factors. You need to be able to explain how and why each factor affects the rate of transpiration.

① Complete 🖉 the sentences using the words in the box.

condenses	diffuses	evaporates	high	low

Water on the surface of cells inside the leaf .... into the air spaces inside

the leaf. This creates a .... concentration of water molecules inside the leaf

compared with the air surrounding the leaf. Therefore, the water vapour ....

out of the leaf through the stomata.

The rate at which the water vapour diffuses out of the leaf depends on the concentration gradient. There are four factors that affect the rate of diffusion: humidity, air movement, light and temperature.

② Number 🖉 the statements in the correct order to give an explanation of how an increase in air movement affects the rate of transpiration. The first one has been done for you.

[1] Increasing air movement carries away more water vapour from near the leaf surface.

[ ] This means the rate of transpiration is higher.

[ ] This increases the concentration gradient between water vapour inside the leaf and water vapour surrounding the leaf.

[ ] This increases the rate of evaporation and diffusion of water vapour out of the stomata.

③ As **light intensity** increases, stomata open more to allow gases to exchange for photosynthesis.

Predict how this would affect the rate of transpiration. Explain 🖉 your prediction.

....

....

....

④ Explain 🖉 why the rate of transpiration increases as the **temperature** increases. Use the terms in the box in your answer.

temperature	energy	evaporate	diffuse	rate	increases	transpiration

....

....

....

....

....

....

Remember If you are explaining why a factor increases or decreases the rate of transpiration, you should use linking words such as 'so' or 'therefore' or 'allowing'.

The rate of evaporation and diffusion increases if the temperature increases because particles at a higher temperature have more kinetic energy.

Unit 2 Plant biology 11

2 **How do I calculate and interpret data on water loss in plants?**

The rate of transpiration can be estimated by measuring the uptake of water by a plant. This can be done by using a potometer.

The diagram shows a potometer. As the plant takes up water, it causes the air bubble to move along the tube.

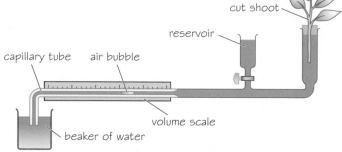

cut shoot

reservoir

capillary tube   air bubble

volume scale

beaker of water

1 Draw ✏ an arrow on the diagram to show the direction in which the bubble will move when the plant transpires.

To calculate the rate of transpiration, you need to know the distance moved by the air bubble and the time taken:

$$\text{rate of transpiration} = \frac{\text{distance moved by the air bubble}}{\text{time taken for the air bubble to move that distance}}$$

> The amount of water a plant takes up is directly related to how much water is lost by the leaves.

A student sets up a potometer. The diagram shows the scale on the capillary tube of the potometer at the start and after 40 minutes.

At start of experiment

capillary tube air bubble

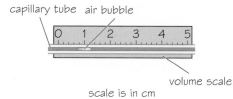

volume scale

scale is in cm

After 40 minutes

capillary tube   air bubble

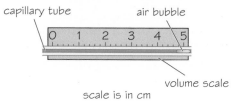

volume scale

scale is in cm

2 **a** What is the position of the air bubble on the capillary tube scale ✏:

i   at the start of the experiment?   ii   after 40 minutes? ....

b How far does the air bubble move in 40 minutes? ✏ ....

c Use these values to calculate ✏ the rate of transpiration. ....

.... cm/minute

3 A student uses a potometer to measure the rate of water uptake by a geranium cutting. She sets up the same apparatus in three different conditions: no wind 10 °C; no wind 20 °C; wind 20 °C.

a Write ✏ the letter of the line on the graph that shows the results for:

i   no wind 10 °C ....

ii   no wind 20 °C ....

iii   wind 20 °C ....

b Sketch ✏ a line on the graph to show the rate of transpiration if the same experiment was done with no wind at 5 °C.

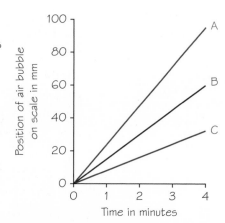

> In which condition, A, B or C, does the air bubble move the furthest in one minute?

3 How do I explain how limiting factors interact?

For graphs showing how rates of photosynthesis are affected by given factors, you need to be able to:

- explain the shapes of the graphs for light intensity, carbon dioxide concentration, temperature and amount of chlorophyll
- understand graphs showing the effect of more than one factor
- identify limiting factors.

1 The graph shows how light intensity affects the rate of photosynthesis. Write 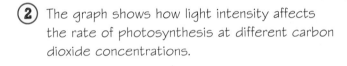 the letters A, B and C in the correct positions on the graph.

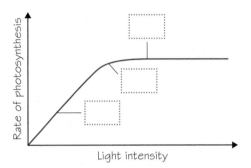

- **A** Carbon dioxide levels begin to limit the reaction
- **B** As light intensity increases, more energy is available and the rate of photosynthesis increases
- **C** No further increase can occur without more CO_2

The straight line in the first part of the graph shows a linear relationship between the light intensity and the rate of photosynthesis. This means that the rate of photosynthesis increases in relation to the light intensity.

When the line levels off, it is showing that the rate of photosynthesis has stopped increasing.

2 The graph shows how light intensity affects the rate of photosynthesis at different carbon dioxide concentrations.

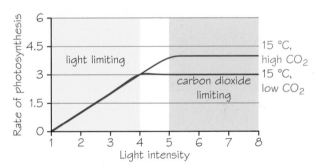

Complete the table by circling the correct words in bold.

When the graph levels off, it shows that the rate of photosynthesis has stopped increasing. One or more factors must be limiting the rate of photosynthesis.

Area of graph	Description	Likely limiting factor
yellow	As the light intensity increases, the rate of photosynthesis **increases / stays the same.** As the concentration of carbon dioxide increases, the rate of photosynthesis **increases / stays the same.**	**Light / carbon dioxide** must be the limiting factor because the graph shows that as the light intensity increases, the rate of photosynthesis increases.
blue	As the light intensity increases, the rate of photosynthesis **increases / stays the same.** As the concentration of carbon dioxide increases, the rate of photosynthesis **increases / stays the same.**	**Light / carbon dioxide** must be the limiting factor because the rate of photosynthesis is higher for the high CO_2 concentration at the same light intensity.

3 Draw a line on the graph in **2** to show a predicted rate of photosynthesis at an even higher carbon dioxide concentration.

Sample response

When calculating the rate of transpiration, you should:
- check you are using the correct values and units
- divide the distance (or volume) by time to calculate the rate.

Look at this exam-style question and the answers given by a student.

Exam-style question

1   A student measured the rate
of transpiration in a leafy twig
using the equipment shown in
Figure 1. She recorded the level
of the top of the air bubble
at 5-minute intervals for
20 minutes. The results are shown
in Table 1.

Time in minutes	0	5	10	15	20
Position of top of air bubble on capillary tube scale in mm	15	21	28	34	40

Table 1

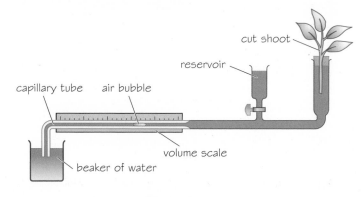

Figure 1

1.1   Explain why the air bubble
moved up the capillary tube.
Because the water was being sucked
up by the leafy twig.   **(1 mark)**

1.2   Calculate the distance moved
along the scale by the air
bubble. _40 mm_   **(1 mark)**

1.3   State the time taken for the bubble to move this distance along the scale.
20 minutes   **(1 mark)**

1.4   Calculate the rate of transpiration.

$$\text{rate of transpiration} = \frac{distance}{time} \text{ so } \frac{40}{20} = 2 \text{ mm per minute}$$ **(1 mark)**

1.5   Explain how increasing air movement would affect the rate of transpiration in a plant.

It would increase it.   **(3 marks)**

---

(1)   The student's answer to **1.1** may not gain any marks because she has used everyday words
instead of technical/scientific terms. Write the name of the process that occurs in plants that

explains why the air bubble moved up the capillary tube. ....

(2)   The answers to **1.2** and **1.4** are incorrect because the student has not interpreted the data
correctly. Circle Ⓐ the mistakes in **1.2** and **1.4** and correct ✎ them.

(3)   The answer to **1.5** would not gain 2 marks because it **describes**
how the transpiration rate is affected by increasing air movement
but does not **explain** it. On paper, write ✎ an answer that
gives reasons why increasing air movement affects the rate of
transpiration.

> The command word 'explain'
> means you must give a reason
> for something happening.

> Think about scientific terms that are likely to be in
> the mark scheme and include these in your answer; for
> example, **diffusion, concentration gradient, water vapour.**

Your turn!

It is now time to use what you have learned to answer the exam-style question from page 9. Remember to read the question thoroughly, looking for information that may help you. Make good use of your knowledge from other areas of biology.

Read the exam-style question and answer it using the hints to guide you.

Exam-style question

1 Figure 1 shows how carbon dioxide concentration affects the rate of photosynthesis in radish plants kept at 16 °C.

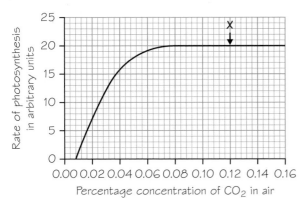

Figure 1

1.1 What is the maximum rate of photosynthesis of the radish plant shown by the graph? **(1 mark)**

....

> Before you attempt to answer a question like this, spend time making sense of the graph. When the line levels out, it means a limiting factor has stopped the rate of photosynthesis increasing.

1.2 Suggest one factor that could be limiting the rate of photosynthesis at point **X**. **(1 mark)**

....

> **Remember** The mnemonic for the factors affecting the rate of photosynthesis is: Leprechauns Can Talk Chinese (Light, Carbon dioxide, Temperature, Chlorophyll).

Radish plants grow best at around 16 °C. Above this temperature, radishes are prone to losing too much water through transpiration.

1.3 Explain why higher temperatures cause an increase in transpiration. **(2 marks)**

....

....

....

> How does temperature affect the movement of particles? What effect would this have on evaporation and diffusion?

Need more practice?

Questions about transpiration and photosynthesis could occur as part of a question about plant structure, plant adaptations, or enhancing conditions in greenhouses, or as stand-alone questions.

Have a go at this exam-style question.

Exam-style question

1 A group of scientists measured the rate of transpiration in a geranium plant at different times of the day. Figure 1 shows their results.

1.1 What was the rate of transpiration in the geranium at 12:00?

.... arbitrary units   **(1 mark)**

The rate of transpiration increased in the geranium between 08:00 and 16:00.

1.2 Calculate the **mean** rate increase per hour in the rate of transpiration between 08:00 and 16:00. Show clearly how you work out your answer.

.... arbitrary units per hour   **(2 marks)**

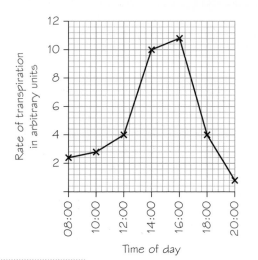

Figure 1

To calculate the average rate increase per hour, you need to calculate the difference between the rates at 08:00 and 16:00 and then divide by the number of hours between those times.

The rate of transpiration in the geranium was the lowest at 20:00.

1.3 On paper, suggest a reason why the rate of transpiration was lowest at 20:00 compared with other times of the day.   **(2 marks)**

Boost your grade

Make sure you can:

• answer questions based on interpreting data about water loss in plants presented in a range of graphs or tables

• confidently explain the effects of different factors on the rate of photosynthesis and use your knowledge and understanding to make predictions if a factor is changed

How confident do you feel about each of these **skills**? Colour in the bars.

1 How do I explain the effect of changing different factors on the rate of transpiration?

2 How do I calculate and interpret data on water loss in plants?

3 How do I explain how limiting factors interact?

③ Genetics and DNA

This unit will help you to construct Punnett square diagrams to work out probabilities and use genetic terms correctly. It will also help you to explain how the structure of DNA affects the proteins made in a cell.

In the exam, you will be asked to answer questions such as the one below.

Exam-style question

1 Fruit flies can have normal or vestigial wings.
A vestigial wing is an abnormally small wing.
Normal-winged fruit flies have the genotype **NN** or **Nn**.
Vestigial-winged flies have the genotype **nn**.

1.1 What causes vestigial wings? (1 mark)

Tick **one** box.

☐ a homozygous dominant genotype ☐ a heterozygous genotype

☐ a homozygous recessive genotype ☐ the environment

A male and a female normal-winged fruit fly were crossed.

They produced 52 offspring. 39 had normal wings and 13 had vestigial wings.

1.2 Draw a Punnett square diagram to show how the ratio of normal-winged and vestigial-winged offspring was produced. (2 marks)

1.3 Determine the probability of two heterozygous normal-winged flies producing a gamete with the genotype **nn**. (1 mark)

1.4 A scientist analysed the DNA in a small segment of a fly gene. The scientist identified four different nucleotide bases in the fly DNA: A, T, C and G.

Explain the importance of these bases in producing a protein. (2 marks)

You will already have done some work on genetics and DNA. Before starting the **skills boosts**, rate your confidence in using Punnett squares, using genetic terms and explaining how the structure of DNA affects the proteins made. Colour in ✏ the bars.

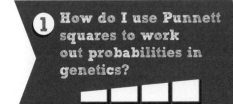

① How do I use Punnett squares to work out probabilities in genetics?

② How do I use genetic terms correctly?

③ How do I explain how the structure of DNA determines what proteins are synthesised?

A chromosome is made from one long DNA molecule. Small sections of the DNA contain genes that contain the coded instructions for making proteins. The proteins are like the 'building blocks' of a body and determine an organism's characteristics.

The genes on a pair of chromosomes may be different because we inherit these genes from both parents. Different versions of the same gene are called **alleles**. If both alleles for one gene are the same, the organism is **homozygous** for the characteristic. If the alleles are different, the organism is **heterozygous**.

(1) Draw a line to link each key word with the correct definition.

Key word	Definition
allele	an allele that shows its effect when in a homozygous or heterozygous genotype
dominant allele	an allele that only shows its effect when in a homozygous genotype
recessive allele	a different version of the same gene

The alleles in an organism are its **genotype**. The physical appearance resulting from the alleles is its **phenotype**.

(2) Tongue-rolling in humans is controlled by a dominant allele (**T**). Non-rolling is controlled by the recessive allele (**t**). A student is **homozygous** for non-tongue-rolling.

a Write the student's genotype. ....

b Write the student's phenotype. ....

> A genotype is the combination of alleles. These alleles are represented using letters. A dominant allele is shown using a capital letter and a recessive allele is shown using a lower-case letter. The dominant allele is always written before the recessive allele, for example, Aa, not aA.

Punnett square diagrams show the possible combinations of genotypes that can occur in offspring when two organisms are crossed. The diagrams show Punnett squares which can be used to predict the probability of different phenotypes.

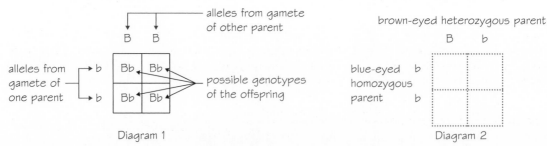

Diagram 1

Diagram 2

(3) Using the information provided, complete diagram 2.

a Start in the first empty box (top left). Look at the letter to its left, and the letter above it. Write both these letters in the box.

> Each box within the Punnett square represents a possible offspring. Each possible offspring will inherit one allele from each parent.

b Write the correct combination of alleles in the remaining three boxes.

c Shade the offspring that will have a phenotype of brown eyes. Use a brown pencil.

d Shade the offspring that will have a phenotype of blue eyes. Use a blue pencil.

1 **How do I use Punnett square diagrams to work out probabilities in genetics?**

Punnett square diagrams help us to understand the possible outcomes when organisms produce offspring. The outcomes of genetic crosses are given as ratios. These ratios can be used to work out the theoretical probability of having offspring with certain characteristics.

1 The allele for tall pea plants is **T**, and the allele for short pea plants is **t**. Two heterozygous dominant pea plants are crossed together.

a Write the genotype from one plant along the top of the Punnett square and the genotype of the other plant down the side.

When you write the gamete genotypes along the sides of the grid, make sure you separate the letters. You should only write one allele on the side of each box because each gamete only contains one, not two, alleles.

It does not matter which parent is on the side or the top of the Punnett square.

b Complete the Punnett square to show the possible alleles of the offspring.

c How many possible outcomes are shown in the diagram? ....

d Circle the offspring that have a genotype that will lead to tall plants.

Remember A heterozygous genotype containing a dominant allele for a trait (Tt, for example) will produce offspring that have the dominant trait.

e How many outcomes will produce tall plants? ....

f How many outcomes will produce short plants? ....

A ratio states how many of the total number of outcomes will have a particular trait.

g What is the ratio of the phenotypes of the offspring? Tick ✓ **one** box.

☐ tall plants to short plants 3:1 ☐ tall plants to short plants 1:4

☐ short plants to tall plants 3:1 ☐ short plants to tall plants 1:4

A ratio can be thought of as a 'for every' statement. For example, there is one black cat for every three brown cats.

In a ratio, the order matters. For example, tall to short in ratio 2:3 means two tall for every three short.

Remember In a ratio, the two numbers need to add up to the total number of outcomes.

The probability of an event happening = $\dfrac{\text{the number of ways it can happen}}{\text{the total number of outcomes}}$

h Complete the table to show the probabilities of the outcomes shown by your Punnett square from a .

Probability is a measure of how likely something is to happen. Probabilities can be written as fractions, decimals or percentages.

Phenotype	Probability		
	Fraction	Decimal	Percentage
Tall plants		0.75	
Short plants	1/4		25%

A probability expressed as a decimal can be converted into a percentage by multiplying the decimal by 100.

To convert a fraction into a decimal, you divide the top number by the bottom number (divide the numerator by the denominator)

2   How do I use genetic terms correctly?

There are many genetic terms you need to know, understand and be able to use correctly. Many of the terms in genetics are closely linked, so it is important to make sure you understand each term and how they are linked.

1. The diagram shows a pair of chromosomes found in a body cell.

   Write 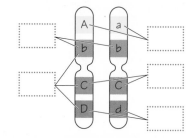 the letters A–E in the correct positions on the diagram.

   A Different genes

   B Heterozygous allele pair

   C Homozygous recessive allele pair

   D Alleles of gene A

   E Homozygous dominant allele pair

   > 'Homo' means the same and 'hetero' means different.

   > **Remember** An allele is a different form of the same gene.

2. The diagram below shows how the structures in genetics are linked.

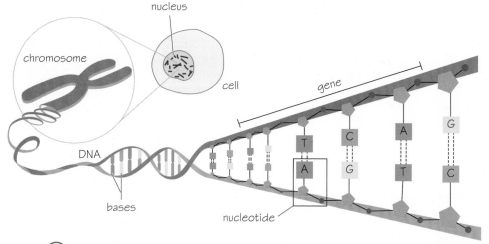

   Write ✏ sentences to explain how the following terms are linked to each other. Use the diagram to help you. The first one has been completed as an example.

   a Nucleus and chromosomes *Chromosomes are found in the nucleus of a cell.*

   > Look at the diagram. A long, coiled molecule forms the shape of the chromosome. What is this molecule?

   b Chromosome and DNA ....

   > A gene contains bases that code for a particular protein. What is the name of the molecule that contains these bases?

   c Gene and DNA ....

   > A nucleotide is made up from a base, a sugar and a phosphate. These nucleotide units can be joined to form a repeating chain that forms a long molecule that is the shape of a ladder.

   d DNA and nucleotide ....

   > Don't confuse a base in DNA with the bases you learn about in chemistry. They are completely different.

   e Base and nucleotide ....

3 How do I explain how the structure of DNA determines what proteins are synthesised?

You need to be able to describe the structure of DNA and be able to interpret diagrams of DNA. You also need to know how the bases in DNA that code for the amino acids are assembled into proteins.

The diagram shows how DNA is a polymer made of repeating units called nucleotides. A nucleotide is made up of a phosphate, a sugar and a base. The nucleotides join to form two strands coiled together forming a double helix.

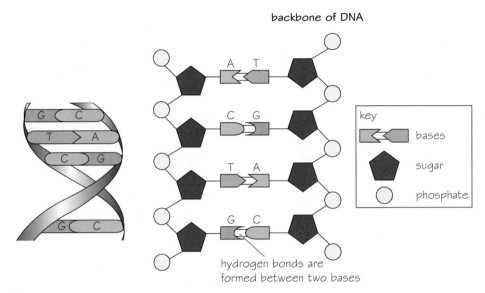

backbone of DNA

key
- bases
- sugar
- phosphate

hydrogen bonds are formed between two bases

DNA is often called a double helix because it is a molecule made from two strands that are joined together by the bases, forming the shape of a double-stranded spiral.

A polymer is a large molecule made up of many small repeating units. DNA is a polymer because it contains many repeating nucleotide units.

1 Use the diagram to help you answer the questions.

a Write ✏ the names of the two parts of a nucleotide that form the 'backbone' of the DNA strand. ....

b Circle Ⓐ and label ✏ a nucleotide within the strand of DNA.

c Circle Ⓐ and label ✏ a base pair.

If you imagine DNA being a bit like a ladder, the backbone would be the sides of the ladder, and the bases form the rungs or steps of the ladder.

The bases pair up. They are described as 'complementary strands' because one base always pairs with only one type of other base. A and T pair up and C and G pair up.

Think of a way to remember which base is linked with which. For example, **A**ll **T**igers **C**an **G**rowl.

2 Write ✏ the complementary base sequence for this base sequence.

C	C	A	T	T	T	A	A	T

It is the order of bases in a gene that determines the order of amino acids in a protein. A sequence of **three** bases provides the code for a particular amino acid. These amino acids are joined together to make different proteins.

3 The amino acid phenylalanine has the base sequence TTT. Proline is CCA and asparagine is AAT.

Write ✏ a base sequence to show the order of bases to code for amino acids in this order: **asparagine   proline   phenylalanine**. The first one has been done for you.

AAT ....

The base sequence in a strand of DNA is continuous, but the bases are always 'read' in sets of three.

Sample response

You may be expected to interpret a diagram of DNA structure and explain how the bases in a gene code for a specific protein.

Look at this exam-style question and the answers given by a student.

Exam-style question

1   Figure 1 shows part of a DNA molecule. It has two strands. Each strand is made up of repeating nucleotide units.

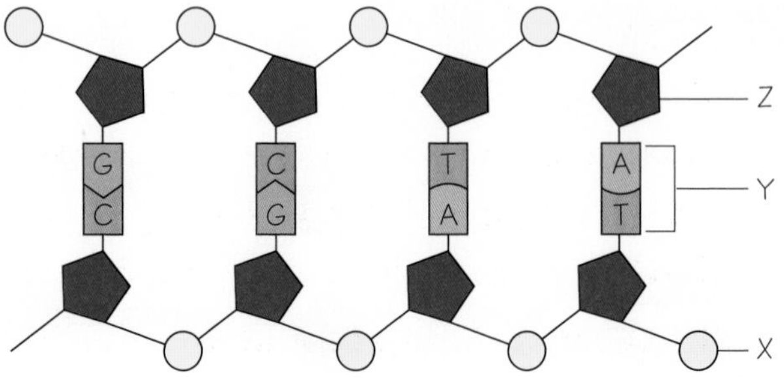

Figure 1

1.1   Which of the following statements is correct? Tick ✓ **one** box.

   ☐ X shows a sugar and Z shows a base

   ☐ X shows a phosphate and Z shows a sugar

   ✓ X shows a sugar and Z shows a phosphate

   ☐ X shows a phosphate and Z shows a gene   **(1 mark)**

1.2   Write the letter of the labelled part of the DNA molecule that contains the instructions for making amino acids. _A gene_   **(1 mark)**

1.3   Explain how the DNA bases in a gene code for a specific protein.

   Each sequence of three DNA bases codes for one specific amino acid.   **(3 marks)**

---

(1) The student's answer to **1.1** was incorrect. Give the correct answer. 🖉

....

Remember The sugar is attached to both the phosphate and the base. It is often represented as a pentagon shape because the molecule forms this shape.

(2) The student has not read **1.2** properly.

   (a) What mistake did the student make? 🖉

....

....

   (b) What is the correct answer?

   Tick ✓ **one** box.   ☐ X   ☐ Y   ☐ Z

A combination of three bases from A, T, C and G code for an amino acid. Amino acids are assembled to make proteins.

(3) Look at the student answer to **1.3**. It only gained 1 out of 3 marks.

   What information is missing for the other 2 marks? Complete 🖉 the sentences to give an answer that would gain 3 marks.

   | Each sequence of three DNA bases codes for one specific amino acid. |
   | Therefore, the order of the bases in the gene determines .... |
   | .... |
   | The order of the amino acids determines .... |

Different proteins are made by assembling amino acids in different orders.

Your turn!

It is now time to use what you have learned to answer the exam-style question from page 17. Remember to read the question thoroughly, looking for information that may help you. Make good use of your knowledge from other areas of biology.

Read the exam-style question and answer it using the hints to guide you.

Exam-style question

1 Fruit flies can have normal or vestigial wings.

A vestigial wing is an abnormally small wing.

Normal-winged fruit flies have the genotype **NN** or **Nn**.

Vestigial-winged flies have the genotype **nn**.

1.1 What causes vestigial wings?

Tick **one** box.

☐ a homozygous dominant genotype

☐ a homozygous recessive genotype

☐ a heterozygous genotype

☐ the environment **(1 mark)**

> Use the information given about the genotypes of the fruit fly to help you answer this question.

> Genetic questions might use organisms or characteristics you have not heard of. This question is testing your ability to apply your knowledge and understanding of genetics. You don't actually need any knowledge about fruit flies or vestigial wings.

A male and a female normal-winged fruit fly were crossed.

They produced 52 offspring. 39 had normal wings and 13 had vestigial wings.

1.2 Draw a Punnett square diagram to show how the ratio of normal-winged and vestigial-winged offspring was produced. **(2 marks)**

> Before you draw the diagram, look at the numbers of flies that had normal wings compared with those that had vestigial wings. What is the ratio? Can you simplify the ratio by dividing both parts by a common factor?

> **Remember** Once you have calculated the ratio, calculate the probability of each type of wing. A cross between two parents with a heterozygous genotype is likely to produce a 3:1 ratio.

1.3 Determine the probability of two heterozygous normal-winged flies producing offspring with the genotype **nn**. **(1 mark)**

1.4 A scientist analysed the DNA in a small segment of a fly gene. The scientist identified four different nucleotide bases in the fly DNA: A, T, C and G.

Explain the importance of these bases in producing a protein. **(2 marks)**

Need more practice?

Exam questions may ask about different parts of a topic, or parts of more than one topic. Questions about genetics and DNA could occur as:
- simple standalone questions about genetic terms or the structure of DNA
- part of a question on inheritance of characteristics, diseases or conditions
- part of a question on how a particular protein is made from DNA.

Have a go at this exam-style question.

Exam-style question

1 Figure 1 shows a small section of a DNA molecule that codes for a protein that is needed to make an enzyme.

| G | C | T | C | C | A | G | T | C | T | A | A | C | A | A |

Figure 1

1.1 How many amino acids does the section of DNA shown in the diagram code for?
Tick **one** box.   **(1 mark)**

☐ 1   ☐ 5   ☐ 7   ☐ 15   **Remember** Each amino acid is coded for by a sequence of three bases.

1.2 What word is used to describe 'a small section of a DNA molecule that codes for a protein'?   **(1 mark)**

1.3 Complete the base sequence shown in Figure 2 for the strand of DNA that would be complementary for the strand shown above.   **(1 mark)**

C ☐ ☐ ☐ ☐ ☐ ☐ ☐ ☐ ☐ ☐ ☐ ☐ ☐ ☐

Figure 2

Remember The bases in DNA match up to specific bases on the opposite strand. A always pairs with T and C always pairs with G.

Boost your grade

To improve your grade, make sure you:
- can confidently explain the differences between different genetic terms and how they are linked
- can interpret family trees to work out genotypes, phenotypes and probabilities of offspring having a particular genotype
- know that different types of mutations can code for altered proteins.

How confident do you feel about each of these **skills**? Colour in the bars.

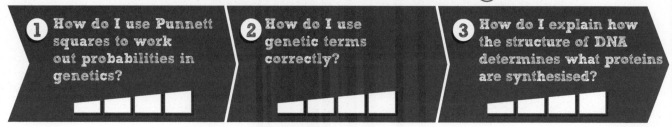

1 How do I use Punnett squares to work out probabilities in genetics?

2 How do I use genetic terms correctly?

3 How do I explain how the structure of DNA determines what proteins are synthesised?

4 Hormones and homeostasis

This unit will help you to explain how the hormones of the menstrual cycle interact. It will also help you to understand how negative feedback works and how control mechanisms lower or raise body temperature.

In the exam, you will be asked to answer questions such as the one below.

Exam-style question

1

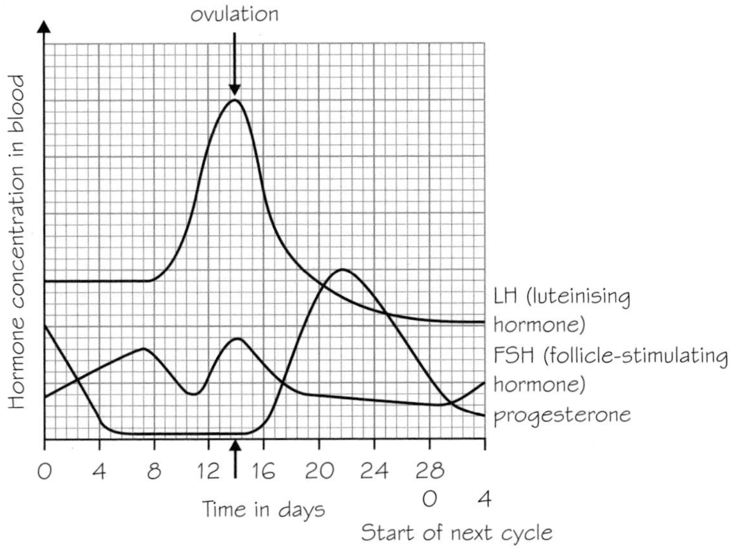

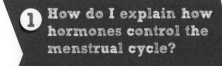

ovulation

Hormone concentration in blood

LH (luteinising hormone)
FSH (follicle-stimulating hormone)
progesterone

0   4   8   12   16   20   24   28
Time in days
0   4
Start of next cycle

Figure 1

1.1 Suggest the stimuli that might cause an egg to be released.

Use information from Figure 1 to justify your answer.   **(3 marks)**

1.2 A high level of oestrogen can inhibit the production of FSH by the pituitary gland.

Explain how this is an example of negative feedback.   **(2 marks)**

1.3 The regulation of body temperature also involves negative feedback. Describe the role of the thermoregulatory centre in maintaining a constant body temperature.   **(2 marks)**

You will already have done some work on hormones and homeostasis. Before starting the **skills boosts**, rate your confidence in explaining the menstrual cycle, negative feedback and controlling body temperature. Colour in (✐) the bars.

1 How do I explain how hormones control the menstrual cycle?

2 How do I explain negative feedback?

3 How do I explain how body temperature is controlled?

Hormones are chemical transmitters that are involved in the control of many bodily processes including the menstrual cycle. The nervous system can also control bodily processes. Homeostasis is the maintenance of constant conditions inside the body. Homeostasis is achieved using a form of control called **negative feedback**.

(1) Complete ✏️ the sentences below about hormones. Select the correct words from the box.

| blood | respiration | skin | hormones | glands | organs | ovulation | oestrogen |

Many bodily processes are controlled by .... These substances are released

by .... and are transported in the .... to their target

.... One example is ...., which is released by the ovaries

and brings about ....

Negative feedback is a form of control that works a bit like the thermostat in your house. If the house gets too warm, the thermostat turns the heating off. The house cools down. When the house gets too cold, the thermostat turns the heating on again, and so on.

(2) Complete ✏️ the flow diagram illustrating negative feedback by writing the correct numbers in the boxes.

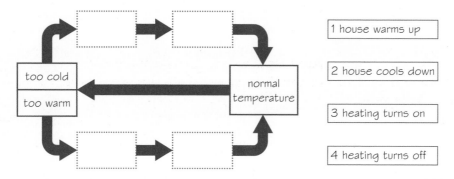

1 house warms up

2 house cools down

3 heating turns on

4 heating turns off

Blood glucose is also controlled by negative feedback. If blood glucose increases above normal, cells in the pancreas release insulin, which stimulates the liver to remove glucose from the blood. If it decreases below normal, other cells in the pancreas release glucagon, which stimulates the liver to release glucose into the blood.

(3) Complete ✏️ the flow diagram by writing the four labels below in the correct boxes.

| insulin | glucagon | glycogen to glucose | glucose to glycogen |

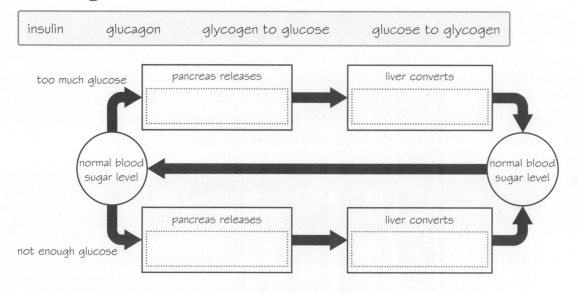

How do I explain how hormones control the menstrual cycle?

The menstrual cycle is a cycle of changes in a woman's reproductive system over about 28 days. Menstruation occurs between days 1 and 5 and then four hormones (**FSH, LH, oestrogen** and **progesterone**) interact to control the maturation and release of a new egg cell from the ovary.

1 Write ✐ the four hormones in the correct boxes in the table below. Use the graph to help you.

FSH   LH   oestrogen   progesterone

....	Increases slightly around day 5 before the egg starts to mature in the follicle.
....	Increases after ovulation on day 14.
....	Peaks sharply as the egg is released and then decreases.
....	Starts to increase before LH levels increase.

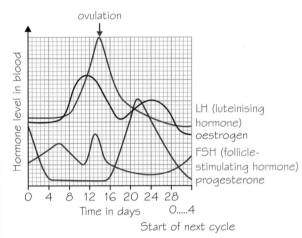

2 Using information from the diagram below, number ✐ the statements in the correct order (1 to 10) to outline the process of the menstrual cycle. The first one has been done for you.

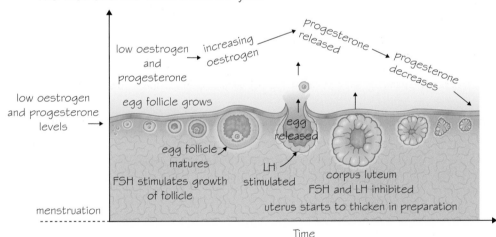

Stimulate means 'to start or increase production of'.
Inhibit means 'to block or decrease production of'.

The **egg follicle** is the part of the ovary where an egg cell grows. A **corpus luteum** is formed from the mature egg follicle once the egg has been released. It then starts to release progesterone.

Low oestrogen and progesterone stimulate menstruation	1	Increased levels of oestrogen stimulate LH production	
Maturing follicle stimulates oestrogen production		Increase in LH stimulates egg release (ovulation)	
Follicle forms corpus luteum and releases progesterone		Increasing oestrogen stimulates thickening of uterus lining	
Oestrogen and progesterone levels start to decrease		Pituitary releases FSH and LH	
FSH and LH release from pituitary is inhibited		FSH stimulates growth and maturation of egg follicle	

2   **How do I explain negative feedback?**

Negative feedback occurs when the rise or fall of a factor brings about changes that return it back to the normal level. Thyroxine production is regulated by negative feedback, which involves the action of other hormones.

Thyroxine is a hormone released by the thyroid gland. It helps to regulate the rate at which energy is transferred from your food to chemical reactions in many types of cells.

1 Circle Ⓐ the statement which best describes the function of thyroxine.

controls blood glucose   regulates basal metabolic rate   increases the heart rate

> Basal metabolic rate is the speed at which chemical reactions take place in the body.

2 The flow chart shows how thyroxine levels are controlled by negative feedback.

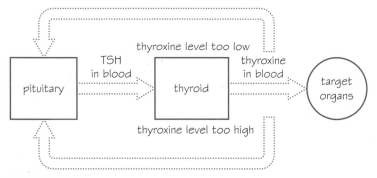

> TSH stands for Thyroid Stimulating Hormone.

On the flow chart:

a Colour 🖉 the glands in yellow.

b Circle Ⓐ the hormones in blue.

c Colour 🖉 the arrow that shows stimulation of thyroxine production in green.

d Colour 🖉 the arrow that shows inhibition of thyroxine production in red.

3 Tick ✓ the correct boxes to show whether these statements about negative feedback are true or false.

> Use the flow chart and follow the arrows.

	True	False
a If the thyroxine level is lower than normal in the blood, then it stimulates the pituitary to release thyroid-stimulating hormone (TSH).	☐	☐
b TSH produced by the pituitary gland will cause a decrease in thyroxine production by the thyroid gland.	☐	☐
c If the thyroxine level is higher than normal in the blood, then a gland in the brain called the pancreas is stimulated.	☐	☐

3 How do I explain how body temperature is controlled?

Automatic responses by the nervous system allow human body temperature to be closely controlled at around 37°C. This creates the best conditions for enzyme action and all cell functions.

① All control systems in the body include **receptors** (cells that detect stimuli), a **coordination centre** (receives impulses from receptors and sends them to effectors) and **effectors** (bring about changes). Draw ✏ lines to show where these are found in the control of body temperature.

receptors that detect changes in the environmental temperature	thermoregulatory centre in the brain
receptors that are sensitive to blood temperature	in the skin
coordination centre	sweat glands, skeletal muscles and muscles within walls of blood vessels
effectors that respond to raise or lower body temperature	within the thermoregulatory centre

② Capillaries do not have any muscle in their walls so they cannot constrict or dilate. The blood vessels that supply the capillaries do contain muscle that can contract to make them constrict. The diagrams show how vasodilation (widening of blood vessels) and vasoconstriction (narrowing of blood vessels) help to control body temperature.

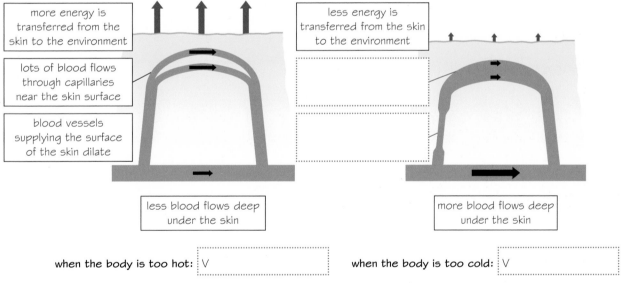

more energy is transferred from the skin to the environment

lots of blood flows through capillaries near the skin surface

blood vessels supplying the surface of the skin dilate

less blood flows deep under the skin

less energy is transferred from the skin to the environment

more blood flows deep under the skin

when the body is too hot: V

when the body is too cold: V

Write ✏ the missing labels in the boxes on the diagram.

③ Circle Ⓐ the correct words in bold to explain how sweating cools the body and shivering warms the body.

Sweat is released from the sweat **muscles / glands**. As sweat **evaporates / cools**, it transfers **energy / heat** from the skin to the surrounding **water / environment**, so the skin cools down. Shivering happens when **skeletal / smooth** muscles contract and relax repeatedly. Increased **movement / respiration** is needed to provide the energy for muscles to contract. Some of the energy **released / made** in respiration also heats up the body.

Sample response

Look at this exam-style question and use the student response to improve your understanding. Consider what the graph is showing and use your knowledge to try to identify the hormones involved. Think about the interaction between the hormones, whether negative feedback is being used to control their actions and how might this help.

Exam-style question

1 Look at Figure 1.

   1.1 Name hormones **W** and **X**. **(2 marks)**

     W: _LH_

     X: _progesterone_

   1.2 Explain how control of LH is an example of negative feedback. **(4 marks)**

     LH causes ovulation and a corpus luteum to form. The corpus luteum releases progesterone.

   1.3 Fertility treatments may use some of the hormones shown in Figure 1.

     Explain why using FSH and LH increases the likelihood of some women becoming pregnant.

     (2 marks)

     FSH causes eggs to mature and LH causes the eggs to be released.

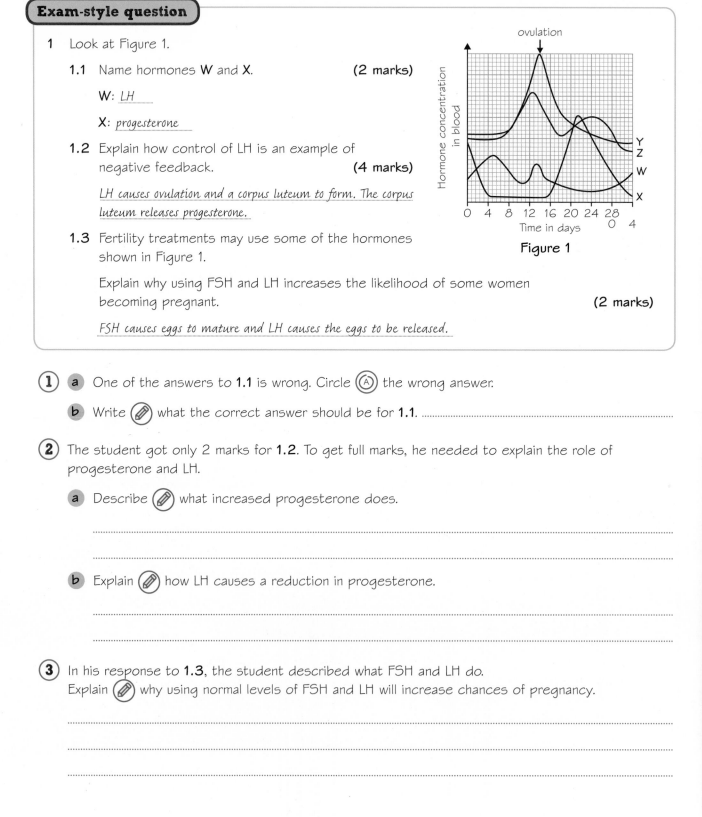

Figure 1

1 **a** One of the answers to **1.1** is wrong. Circle Ⓐ the wrong answer.

   b Write 🖉 what the correct answer should be for **1.1**. ....

2 The student got only 2 marks for **1.2**. To get full marks, he needed to explain the role of progesterone and LH.

   a Describe 🖉 what increased progesterone does.

   ....

   ....

   b Explain 🖉 how LH causes a reduction in progesterone.

   ....

   ....

3 In his response to **1.3**, the student described what FSH and LH do. Explain 🖉 why using normal levels of FSH and LH will increase chances of pregnancy.

....

....

....

Your turn!

It is now time to use what you have learned to answer the exam-style question from page 25. Remember to read the question thoroughly, looking for information that may help you. Make good use of your knowledge from other areas of biology.

Read the exam-style question and answer it using the hints to guide you.

Exam-style question

1

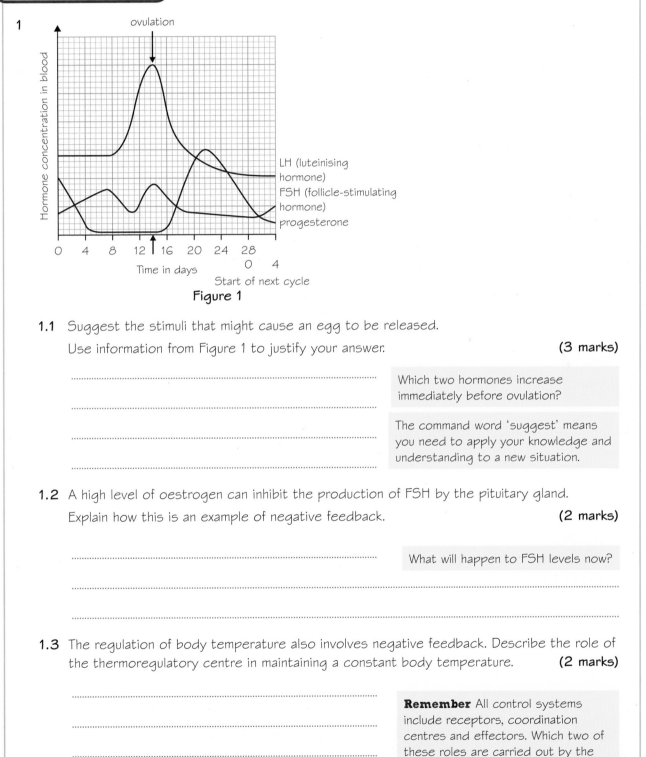

Figure 1

1.1 Suggest the stimuli that might cause an egg to be released.

Use information from Figure 1 to justify your answer. **(3 marks)**

....

....

....

....

> Which two hormones increase immediately before ovulation?

> The command word 'suggest' means you need to apply your knowledge and understanding to a new situation.

1.2 A high level of oestrogen can inhibit the production of FSH by the pituitary gland.

Explain how this is an example of negative feedback. **(2 marks)**

....

....

....

> What will happen to FSH levels now?

1.3 The regulation of body temperature also involves negative feedback. Describe the role of the thermoregulatory centre in maintaining a constant body temperature. **(2 marks)**

....

....

....

....

> **Remember** All control systems include receptors, coordination centres and effectors. Which two of these roles are carried out by the thermoregulatory centre?

Need more practice?

Questions about homeostasis and hormones could occur as part of a question on how a treatment or drug might influence the hormones, or as a stand-alone question.

Have a go at this exam-style question.

1 Figure 1 shows how core body temperature is controlled.

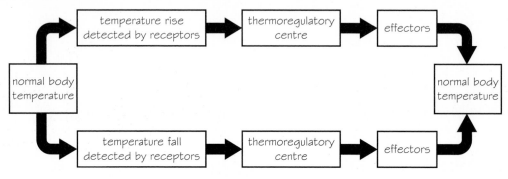

Figure 1

1.1 Using Figure 1 and your own knowledge, explain why temperature control is an example of negative feedback. **(2 marks)**

....

....

1.2 Explain how a temperature change detected by receptors leads to a response in the effectors. **(3 marks)**

....

....

....

1.3 On paper, describe the effectors that respond when core body temperature increases. Explain how these effectors bring about a return to normal body temperature. **(4 marks)**

Boost your grade

Practise drawing sketch graphs of menstrual cycle hormone concentrations over 28 days.

Draw the negative feedback flow diagram next to an exam question before answering.

Be able to explain how control mechanisms raise or lower body temperature in different situations.

How confident do you feel about each of these **skills**? Colour in 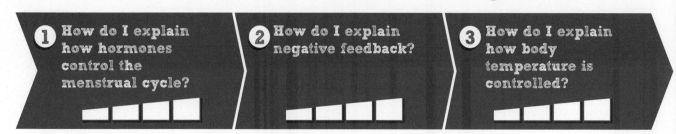 the bars.

1 How do I explain how hormones control the menstrual cycle?

2 How do I explain negative feedback?

3 How do I explain how body temperature is controlled?

⑤ Variation and evolution

This unit will help you to understand why genetic variation is important and how evolution can sometimes lead to new species. It will also help you to explain how the theory of evolution developed over time.

In the exam, you will be asked to answer questions such as the one below.

Exam-style question

1   Figure 1 shows a giant anteater.

The giant anteater has a long tongue and a narrow head. It feeds on insects found inside holes.

The giant anteater evolved from an ancestor which had a short tongue and a rounded head.

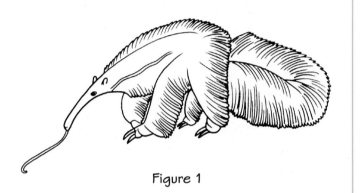

Figure 1

1.1   Explain how the giant anteater may have evolved from its ancestor.   (4 marks)

1.2   The giant anteater reproduces by sexual reproduction.

Explain why sexual reproduction would be an advantage to the anteater if the environment changes.   (2 marks)

You will have already done some work on reproduction and evolution. Before starting the **skills boosts**, rate your confidence in each area. Colour in ⟨🖉⟩ the bars.

① How do I explain the advantages and disadvantages of asexual and sexual reproduction?

② How do I explain how the theory of evolution developed?

③ How do I explain the steps that give rise to a new species?

Evolution is a change in the inherited characteristics of a population over time. It happens through a process called natural selection. Eventually, evolution may result in the formation of a new species.

For evolution to happen, there must be genetic variation in a population. Sexual reproduction plays an important role in producing genetic variation.

(1) a Sexual reproduction involves two parents. How many parents are involved in asexual

reproduction? (✏️) ....

> Cell division is important in reproduction. **Meiosis** is the type of cell division that produces non-identical daughter cells. These cells become gametes (sex cells). **Mitosis** always produces identical cells.

b Circle (Ⓐ) the type of reproduction that matches the statements in the table.

Involves the fusion of male and female gametes	Asexual / Sexual
Offspring are genetically identical	Asexual / Sexual
Genetic information is mixed, leading to variety in offspring	Asexual / Sexual
Involves meiosis	Asexual / Sexual
Involves mitosis	Asexual / Sexual

Sexual reproduction brings together new **combinations** of existing varieties of genes. Different forms of a gene are called alleles. New alleles can be produced by **mutations** in DNA.

c Bacteria reproduce by binary fission, which is a type of **asexual** reproduction. Their offspring occasionally show genetic variation. Circle (Ⓐ) the best word to explain what causes this variation.

mitosis	mutation	gametes

In the process of natural selection, individuals with characteristics most suited to the environment are more likely to survive and breed successfully. Selective breeding also causes changes in a population. This is an artificial process in which humans breed plants and animals for particular genetic characteristics.

(2) Draw (✏️) lines to show if the changes in populations described are due to natural selection or selective breeding.

When food is in short supply, only those giraffes with longer necks survive because they can reach leaves high in trees.

> Environmental variation is the differences in individuals that develop in their lifetime. This cannot be inherited and is not due to selective breeding or natural selection.

Milk yields of dairy cows increased by 20% between 2000 and 2016.

Selective breeding

When air pollution made tree trunks black, dark peppered moths were less likely than pale peppered moths to be eaten by birds, so more dark moths survived to breed.

Natural selection

New varieties of plants with large and unusual petals are being developed by flower growers.

1 How do I explain the advantages and disadvantages of asexual and sexual reproduction?

To explain the advantages or disadvantages of each type of reproduction, you must first be able to identify them. You may need to explain them in the context of unfamiliar organisms.

1. Asexual reproduction is faster than sexual reproduction. Tick ✓ the boxes in the table to identify each of these other advantages as belonging to asexual or sexual reproduction.

Advantage	Asexual	Sexual
only one parent needed		
produces variation in the offspring		
if the environment changes, variation gives a survival advantage by natural selection of better suited varieties		
more time and energy efficient – no need to find a mate		
many identical offspring can be produced quickly to take advantage of favourable conditions		

2. Explain the advantages and disadvantages of each type of reproduction using this information.

Remember Only sexual reproduction produces offspring by combining genes from two parents.

Anemones are animals that usually live permanently attached to rocks in shallow sea water. Explain the advantages and disadvantages of asexual reproduction to anemones.

Student A In asexual reproduction only one parent is needed. This is an advantage because anemones don't move around so it might be difficult to find a mate.

a. The student explained an advantage of asexual reproduction. Underline (A) the information in the question box that the student used in their explanation.

b. The student also explained a disadvantage. Complete ✏ the answer.

One disadvantage of asexual reproduction is that there is no genetic variation in offspring, so if the environment changes

....

....

An advantage of one type of reproduction can be rewritten as a disadvantage for the other type of reproduction.

Cichlids are fish that reproduce by sexual reproduction. They live in lakes where the conditions often change over time. Explain one advantage and one disadvantage of sexual reproduction to cichlid fish.

c. Fill in ✏ the gaps to complete this student answer.

Advantage: Sexual reproduction produces .... in offspring, so when the environment changes some varieties might be better suited to the new conditions. Natural selection will help the population to ....

Disadvantage: Sexual reproduction is .... than asexual reproduction. This is a disadvantage because the cichlids would not be able to make the most of .... conditions by producing lots of .... quickly.

2 **How do I explain how the theory of evolution developed?**

Scientific theories often change over time. Initial evidence may be incomplete and new data from experiments or observations gathered from many scientists can either support or challenge earlier ideas. You should be able to explain how the theory of evolution developed and why it was only gradually accepted.

1 Read the account of how the theory of evolution developed, then answer the questions.

In the 18th century, most people believed that all living things on Earth had been created by God and had remained relatively unchanged. Jean-Baptiste Lamarck was one of the first scientists to suggest that species evolve, or change over time. Lamarck thought that changes that happen to an organism during its lifetime can be inherited, but later experiments did not show this. Charles Darwin proposed the theory of evolution by the mechanism of natural selection, after examining fossils and observing living things on his travels around the world, backed up by years of experimentation. At the same time, after collecting evidence worldwide, Alfred Russel Wallace independently proposed that species evolve because only the fittest survive to breed. Fifty years later, the discovery of genes explained the mechanism of inheritance and variation. It also explained why Lamarck's ideas were mostly incorrect.

a Underline Ⓐ the initial idea of Lamarck that was supported by both Darwin and Wallace.

b Highlight 🖉 the part of Lamarck's theory that was challenged by later scientists because evidence did not support it.

c New information (data) is needed if a theory is to be changed.
Circle Ⓐ three ways in which Darwin gathered new data.

d How did Wallace's work help to develop the theory of evolution?

....

....

....

e Circle Ⓐ the correct answers in **bold**.

The later discovery of genes **supported / challenged** the ideas of Darwin and Wallace

because it explained why organisms showed **inherited variation / environmental variation**

and led to the theory being more widely **accepted / rejected**.

2 Draw lines 🖉 to complete the sentences that explain why the theory of evolution by natural selection, as proposed by Darwin and Wallace, was only gradually accepted.

The Church objected to the theory because it challenged the idea that	50 years after the theory was published.
The causes of variation and the mechanism of inheritance were not known until	there was still not enough evidence, such as certain fossils, to convince many scientists.
At the time the theory was published	God made all the animals and plants that live on Earth.

③ How do I explain the steps that give rise to a new species?

Over billions of years, evolution has given rise to all the species on Earth from early simple single-celled lifeforms. Different environments may result in several species evolving from one ancestor.

① Evolution does not always go so far as to result in a new species. Exam questions may ask you only to explain how natural selection has caused changes in a population. Alternatively, you may be asked to explain how a new species has arisen. These steps are important to consider:

☐ **A** There is isolation or separation of different populations.

☐ **B** There are differences or changes in environmental conditions.

☐ **C** There is genetic variation in the population (from mutations).

☐ **D** Individuals with characteristics most suited to the environment are more likely to survive.

> Isolation is only important when explaining how different species arise, not when explaining natural selection within one species.

☐ **E** These individuals reproduce more successfully.

☐ **F** The alleles for these favourable characteristics are passed on to the next generation.

☐ **G** Eventually, new species may develop if the populations become so different that they are unable to breed successfully with each other.

> In this example, the use of antibiotics is a change in the environment, but no new species arise.

a Antibiotics are widely used to treat bacterial diseases. Natural selection has resulted in an increase in antibiotic-resistant populations of bacteria. Tick ✓ the boxes to show which of the steps **A** to **G** would be relevant to this question.

b If new species arise, all the steps are important. Highlight ✐ the most important words (maximum three words) in each step **A** to **G**.

Learn these words to remind you of the important steps to use in this type of question.

② Circle Ⓐ the correct words in bold below to explain what happens when a new species forms.

> If two **populations / individuals** of one species become so different that they can no longer interbreed to produce **living / fertile** offspring, they have formed two new **species / varieties**.

Your answer must also **be specific to the example** given. Look at this exam-style question.

Exam-style question

1 Two main species of elephant are alive today. These are the African elephant and the Asian elephant. Both can live in similar habitats, although Asian elephants experience cooler, wetter conditions. Both are thought to have evolved from *Primelephas*, an extinct species. Explain how the modern elephant species may have evolved from this common ancestor. **(4 marks)**

The answer is about new species arising and so should mention all the steps in ① above. It should also include explanation specific to the example as shown below.

③ **a** Circle Ⓐ the best answer to explain how the *Primelephas* populations were isolated.

> different geographical areas   different behaviour   on different small islands

b Circle Ⓐ the most likely differences in environmental conditions between the two populations.

> food type   predators   pollution   habitat   climate

> Look for hints in the question.

Sample response

To explain an example of evolution by natural selection, a good answer should mention all the relevant steps in a logical order using information provided to make it specific to the example. You may also need to explain how different scientists contributed to the development of the theory.

Exam-style question

1 Warfarin is a poison that is used to kill rats. Over time, the rat population has become more resistant to warfarin.

Use Darwin's theory of natural selection to explain the development of warfarin resistance in the rat population. **(4 marks)**

Student A | *If the rats are given warfarin poison, only those rats that are resistant to warfarin will survive. Some rats might have a mutation that makes them resistant to warfarin. The ones without the mutation will die. The resistant rats are more likely to have offspring and will pass on the resistance allele to the next generation. So, there will now be more warfarin resistant rats in the population.*

Each of these steps gained a mark:
- There is genetic **variation** in the population.
- Individuals with characteristics **most suited** to the environment are more likely to **survive**.
- These individuals **reproduce more successfully**.
- The **alleles** for these favourable characteristics are **passed on** to the next generation.

(1) This is a good answer. Do you think that student A gained all 4 marks? (A) **Yes / No**

(2) Annotate student A's answer as follows:
   a Underline (A) the words that describe the genetic variation in the rat population.
   b Highlight (✏) the change in the environment that caused natural selection.
   c Circle (A) the characteristic that made some rats better suited to the new environment.

Student B | *If a rat gets small doses of poison over its lifetime it may become immune to the poison and pass this on to its babies.*

(3) This answer gained no marks. Circle (A) the correct **bold** words to explain why it gained no marks.

The answer is based on the theory of **Lamarck / Wallace** and not on Darwin's theory of natural selection. Lamarck's theory was shown to be **wrong / correct** because changes that occur in an organism during its lifetime **can / cannot** be inherited.

Remember Evolution is about changes in populations, not changes in individuals.

Exam-style question

2 Antibiotics are widely used to treat bacterial diseases. Explain how natural selection has resulted in an increase in antibiotic-resistant populations of bacteria. **(4 marks)**

Student C | *Some bacteria are better able to survive the antibiotics, these bacteria will reproduce more.*

(4) This answer gained 2 marks. On paper, use the mark scheme from **1** to help you to re-write (✏) this answer to gain 4 marks. Make sure it is specific to the example of bacteria and antibiotics.

Your turn!

It is now time to use what you have learned to answer the exam-style question from page 33. Remember to read the question thoroughly, looking for information that may help you. Make good use of your knowledge from other areas of biology.

Read the exam-style question and answer it using the hints to guide you.

Exam-style question

1   **Figure 1** shows a giant anteater.

The giant anteater has a long tongue and a narrow head. It feeds on insects found inside holes.

The giant anteater evolved from an ancestor which had a short tongue and a rounded head.

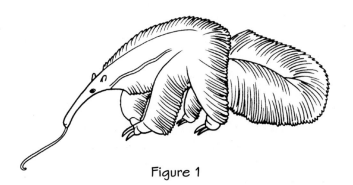

Figure 1

1.1   Explain how the giant anteater may have evolved from its ancestor.   **(4 marks)**

....

....

....

....

Write your answer as four sentences to mention each of the following points: variation, what characteristics are favourable in this example and why, survival/breeding success, and what is passed on.

....

....

....

....

1.2   The giant anteater reproduces by sexual reproduction.

Explain why sexual reproduction would be an advantage to the anteater if the environment changes.   **(2 marks)**

....

....

....

....

What does sexual reproduction provide in offspring? What process is then able to happen? How does this help the population?

....

Need more practice?

Questions about variation and evolution could occur as part of a question on how new species arise, or how one species changes over time, or as stand-alone questions.

Have a go at this exam-style question.

Exam-style question

1   When Charles Darwin visited the Galapagos Islands, he studied a group of birds called finches.

The finches that first arrived in the Galapagos ate seeds and had medium-sized beaks.

The warbler finch is one type of finch found on some Galapagos islands today. It has a narrow beak and eats insects.

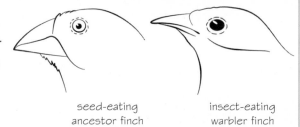

seed-eating ancestor finch   insect-eating warbler finch

Figure 2

1.1   There are 13 different species of finch on the Galapagos Islands.

Suggest how so many different species may have evolved from a single ancestor species.   (2 marks)

....

....

1.2   Use Darwin's theory of natural selection to explain how the insect-eating finch may have evolved from the seed-eating finch.   (4 marks)

....

....

....

....

1.3   All the Galapagos finch species have similar DNA to a single species from the mainland. Explain how this supports Darwin's theory of how the finches evolved.   (2 marks)

....

....

Boost your grade

To improve your grade you should be able to:
• evaluate the life cycle of an organism, comparing the advantages and disadvantages of asexual and sexual reproduction
• explain how mutations bring about variation by changing amino acid sequences.

How confident do you feel about each of these **skills**? Colour in the bars.

1 How do I explain the advantages and disadvantages of asexual and sexual reproduction?

2 How do I explain how the theory of evolution developed?

3 How do I explain the steps that give rise to a new species?

6 Cloning cells and organisms

This unit will help you to understand how adult cells can be cloned to produce embryos and to compare the risks and benefits of the medical use of stem cells produced in therapeutic cloning. It will also help you to understand how monoclonal antibodies are made from a single clone of cells.

In the exam, you will be asked to answer questions such as the one below.

Exam-style question

1 Adult cell cloning can be used to produce embryos that are clones of animals, including humans.

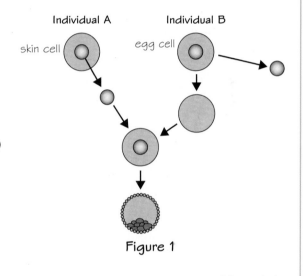

Figure 1

1.1 Use information from Figure 1 and your own knowledge to describe how adult cell cloning could be used to produce a cloned embryo. **(4 marks)**

1.2 Therapeutic cloning produces embryos which are cloned from the body cells of a patient. Stem cells from a cloned embryo could be used to replace damaged cells in patients with diabetes. Explain one advantage and one disadvantage of treating diabetes with this type of stem cell. **(4 marks)**

1.3 Monoclonal antibodies are also used in medical treatments. Cloned hybridoma cells are used to produce monoclonal antibodies. Name the two types of cell that are fused to make a hybridoma cell. **(2 marks)**

You will already have done some work on cloning, stem cells and monoclonal antibodies. Before starting the **skills boosts**, rate your confidence in these topics. Colour in 🖉 the bars.

1 How do I describe the main stages of adult cell cloning?	2 How do I evaluate the use of stem cells in medicine?	3 How do I describe how monoclonal antibodies are produced?

Cloning occurs when a genetically identical copy of a cell or organism is made. Cloning can be used to make lots of copies of plants, animals or cells that have useful properties. Cloning also occurs naturally, such as in asexual reproduction, identical twins and division of cells for growth or repair.

1 A common mistake is to confuse cloning with genetic engineering. For each example, decide if it is genetic engineering (GE) or cloning (C). Write 🖉 'C' or 'GE' in each box. One has been done for you.

a Taking cuttings of plants

b Adding a disease-resistant gene to a cotton plant

c Splitting a cow embryo into cells for embryo transplants

d Producing offspring by mitosis

e Culturing a stem cell so it divides to make lots of new cells

f Correcting a mutation in DNA that causes a disease

g Changing a bacterium so that it will make human insulin

C

> Cloning makes copies; the genes and DNA stay the same. Genetic engineering modifies (changes) the genes or DNA of cells or organisms.

2 Adult cell cloning can be used to make cloned embryos.
Circle Ⓐ the best definition of 'adult cell' when used to describe cloning.

cell from a person older than sixteen	unspecialised cell

body cell from a child or adult, but not from an embryo

3 Complete 🖉 the sentences to explain what stem cells are. Choose words from the box.

> Differentiation means changing to become a specialised cell. A differentiated cell does a certain job and usually stops dividing.

differentiation   meristems   marrow   divide

A stem cell is an undifferentiated cell which can .... to make

many more cells of the same type. Other types of cell can arise from stem cells

by .... Stem cells are found in embryos, in some adult tissues such as

bone .... and in the .... of plants.

4 Lymphocytes are a type of white blood cell that releases antibodies to help in the fight against a disease. Antibodies are proteins that can attach to disease-causing organisms (such as bacteria) and trigger responses that lead to the destruction of the organism. Label 🖉 the diagram to show an antigen, antibody, bacterium and lymphocyte.

> Antibodies join to a binding site on a specific antigen. Antigens are proteins; specific antigens cover the surface of a bacterium.

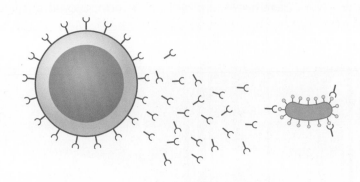

1   How do I describe the main stages of adult cell cloning?

Adult cells can be cloned to produce embryos. These embryos can be used to make stem cells, or to make a whole new individual. This skills boost looks at how these cloned embryos are made.

1. Two cells are needed for adult cell cloning: a body cell from the individual to be cloned and an unfertilised egg cell. Draw 🖊 lines to link the boxes that explain why each type of cell is used.

Only the nucleus of this cell is needed.

Special conditions inside this type of cell allow an embryo to develop.

adult cell – a body cell from the individual to be cloned (often a skin cell)

unfertilised egg cell

The DNA from this cell carries the genetic information needed to make the clone.

The nucleus of this cell is discarded because its DNA is not needed.

The clone will be genetically identical to the adult cell. Genetic information is contained in the nucleus.

2. These two cells are treated to produce a cloned embryo using three main stages.

Stage 1: The nucleus is removed from the unfertilised egg cell.

Stage 2: The nucleus from the adult skin cell is inserted into the egg cell.

Stage 3: An electric shock stimulates the egg cell to divide to form an embryo. The embryo has the same genetic information as the adult skin cell.

a) Label 🖊 the diagram with the number of each stage to show where it happens.

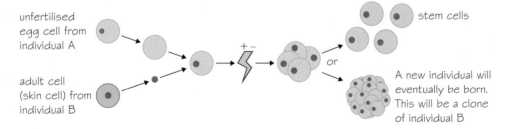

unfertilised egg cell from individual A

adult cell (skin cell) from individual B

stem cells

or

A new individual will eventually be born. This will be a clone of individual B

b) Embryos cloned in this way can be used to produce a whole new cloned individual (not allowed for humans), or the cells of the embryo can be used to make stem cells.

Label 🖊 the diagram above with the correct letters to show what happens in each case.

X The embryo, now a ball of cells, is placed into the womb of an adult female to develop.

Y The cells of the embryo are separated and cultured.

When adult cell cloning is used to produce stem cells for use in medicine, this is called therapeutic cloning.

2   How do I evaluate the use of stem cells in medicine?

The command word **evaluate** means that you must consider the arguments for and against, using your own knowledge and any evidence that is provided. Different types of stem cells have different advantages (benefits) and disadvantages (risks).

(1) Stem cells used in medicine can be adult stem cells (such as from bone marrow) or stem cells from embryos. The table shows some evidence for each type of stem cell. Decide if the evidence describes an advantage (**A**) or a disadvantage (**D**). Circle Ⓐ your answer.

Embryonic stem cells		Adult stem cells	
Replace faulty cells with healthy cells.	Ⓐ / D	Replace faulty cells with healthy cells.	A / D
Can differentiate into any type of cell.	A / D	Will differentiate into only a few types of cell.	A / D
An embryo is destroyed – an ethical issue because some people believe embryos have a right to life.	A / D	No embryo is destroyed – fewer ethical and religious objections.	A / D
Stem cells can be contaminated and transfer viral infections.	A / D	Stem cells can be contaminated and transfer viral infections.	A / D
Therapeutic cloning can produce embryos with the same genes as the patient, so stem cells are not rejected by the patient's body.	A / D	It may be difficult to take adult stem cells from a person who is ill. The patient's body may reject stem cells from another person.	A / D

(2) To evaluate, you must give a balanced argument. This means that you must mention advantages and disadvantages of each type of stem cell and make comparisons where relevant. Write 🖉 an evaluation using the steps in the hint boxes and evidence from (1) to help you.

(a) Describe 🖉 one similarity in the advantages and disadvantages of the types of stem cell.

....

....

....

> Look for an advantage or disadvantage shown by both types of stem cell.

(b) Describe 🖉 a difference in the advantages and disadvantages of the types of stem cell.

....

....

> Describe a disadvantage of adult stem cells and explain why embryonic stem cells provide an advantage in this case.

....

....

> Describe a disadvantage of embryonic stem cells and explain why adult stem cells provide an advantage in this case.

....

You now need to finish your evaluation with a conclusion that is justified (explained).

(3) Highlight 🖉 the conclusion and underline Ⓐ the justification in this student response.

> Overall, embryonic stem cells are a better option for replacing faulty cells because they can provide a wider variety of cells and will not be rejected if made by therapeutic cloning but they do raise greater ethical concerns.

> Usually, the conclusion that is made does not matter as long as it is well argued.

> Use comparison words for a better evaluation, such as: however, although, both, only, whereas, in contrast, unlike.

③ **How do I describe how monoclonal antibodies are produced?**

Monoclonal antibodies can be made that bind to any specific antigen. They are used in medical diagnosis and treatments. To describe how they are produced, you need to understand each stage and write about them in a logical order, using the correct key terms.

① Producing monoclonal antibodies involves several types of cell. Match ✐ each type of cell to its description.

| lymphocyte ⦂ | ⦂cell made by fusing a lymphocyte and a tumour cell |

| tumour cell ⦂ | ⦂cell that divides over and over again to form a clump of cells |

| hybridoma ⦂ | ⦂white blood cell that produces antibodies |

② Write ✐ each key term from the box next to its definition.

| antibody   antigen   binding site   cloned   monoclonal | See page 42 for help. |

a Protein that joins to a single binding site on an antigen. ....

b Protein that has a specific shape that an antibody will attach to. ....

c Area on an antigen that a specific antibody can chemically attach to. ....

d A cell is caused to divide to make many identical cells. ....

e Identical antibodies made by a single clone of cells. ....

③ The diagram shows the general method of how monoclonal antibodies are made.

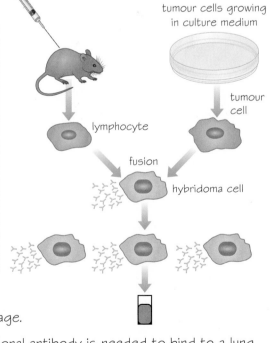

tumour cells growing in culture medium

lymphocyte

tumour cell

fusion

hybridoma cell

1 A specific antigen is injected into a mouse. This stimulates mouse lymphocytes to make the correct antibody.

2 Lymphocytes are collected from the mouse.

3 Lymphocytes are combined with a tumour cell to make a hybridoma cell. The hybridoma cell can both divide and make the antibody.

4 A single **hybridoma / cancer** cell is cloned to produce many **identical / varied** cells that all produce **different / the same** antibodies.

5 A large amount of the antibody can now be collected and purified.

a Circle Ⓐ the correct words in stage 4.

b Add ✐ numbers to the diagram to show each stage.

c What would be injected into the mouse if a monoclonal antibody is needed to bind to a lung cancer cell? ✐ ....
    Specific proteins are found on the surface of all cells.

d Why are hybridoma cells needed to produce monoclonal antibodies? ✐ ....

....

Lymphocyte cells produce antibodies, but few of these can be extracted from the mouse.

Unit 6 Cloning cells and organisms   **45**

Sample response

To describe the process of animal cloning, look for clues in the question to decide what type of cloning is taking place. Describe relevant stages in a logical order using any information provided.

Exam-style question

1   Read this extract from a newspaper article about cloning.

> The Pyrenean ibex is a type of wild goat that recently became extinct. A skin cell from the last remaining Pyrenean ibex was cloned in an attempt to save the species. A domestic goat was used to provide the egg cell required. Another domestic goat gave birth to the cloned Pyrenean ibex. Unfortunately, the baby ibex died soon after birth.

1.1   Describe how adult cell cloning could be used to clone the Pyrenean ibex.   **(5 marks)**

Compare these two student responses.

Student A

The middle of an unused egg cell is taken out. It is replaced with a nucleus taken from the ibex skin cell. When the ibex baby has started to develop it is put inside the belly of a domestic goat where it can continue to grow.

Student B

The nucleus is taken from the ibex skin cell and inserted into the unfertilised egg cell. The nucleus of the egg cell from the domestic goat is removed. The egg cell will start to divide and form an ibex embryo. When it has become a ball of cells, it is placed in the womb of an adult female goat to continue its development.

(1) Student B gained more marks than Student A. This was partly because they used the correct scientific words.

   a   Highlight 🖊 words in Student A's answer that should be replaced with more scientific words.

   b   List 🖊 the scientific words that could have been used instead of the words that you highlighted.

....

(2) Student B has not written down the stages of adult cell cloning in the most logical order.

   a   Circle Ⓐ one sentence that should be moved to give the correct order.

   b   Draw an arrow 🖊 on the student answer to show where it should be moved to.

(3) Both students failed to gain a mark for describing how the egg cell is made to divide into an embryo. How is the egg cell made to divide? 🖊

| What is applied to the egg cell to stimulate it to the divide? |

....

....

(4) Label 🖊 the answer from Student B to show where you would add your answer to (3) so that Student B would gain full marks.

Your turn!

It is now time to use what you have learned to answer the exam-style question from page 41. Remember to read the question thoroughly, looking for information that may help you. Make good use of your knowledge from other areas of biology.

Exam-style question

1 Adult cell cloning can be used to produce embryos that are clones of animals, including humans.

1.1 Use information from **Figure 1** and your own knowledge to describe how adult cell cloning could be used to produce a cloned embryo. **(4 marks)**

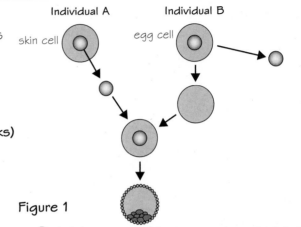

Individual A   Individual B

skin cell   egg cell

Figure 1

---

(1) Use these questions to help you to structure your answer to **1.1**.

a What is taken from the individual that is to be cloned? ....

b What is the first step in modifying the unfertilised egg cell taken from another individual?

....

c What is the second step in modifying this egg cell? ....

....

d How is the modified egg cell treated and why? ....

....

(2) Now write your complete answer to **1.1** on paper.

Exam-style question

1.2 Therapeutic cloning produces embryos which are cloned from the body cells of a patient. Stem cells from these cloned embryos could be used to replace damaged cells in patients with diabetes. Explain one advantage and one disadvantage of treating diabetes with this type of stem cell. **(4 marks)**

> Not all stem cells are produced using the patient's own cells. Not all stem cells come from embryos.

....

....

1.3 Monoclonal antibodies are also used in medical treatments. Cloned hybridoma cells are used to produce monoclonal antibodies. Name the two types of cell that are fused to make a hybridoma cell. **(2 marks)**

> The hybridoma cell combines a cell that produces antibodies with a cell that divides repeatedly.

....

Need more practice?

Exam questions may ask about different parts of a topic, or parts of more than one topic. Questions about cloning cells and organisms could occur as:

- part of a question on how cloning is used in agriculture, conservation or medicine
- part of a question about an experiment or investigation.

Have a go at this exam-style question.

Exam-style question

1 Type 1 diabetes is a condition in which the patient's pancreas produces little or no insulin. This results in glucose imbalance, causing damage to body organs. Read the information in the box.

> Insulin injections have been used for many years as a treatment for diabetes. Patients check their blood glucose levels and inject insulin at least three times a day. Blood glucose levels are difficult to control effectively with insulin injections, so some damage to organs still occurs.
>
> Tests are taking place on a new treatment, using stem cells taken from a spare embryo from IVF. The patients also take drugs to stop their immune systems from attacking the stem cells. The stem cells are placed in a container then implanted under the skin. The cells should respond to the patient's blood glucose levels, producing insulin when needed and keeping blood glucose within safe levels.

1.1 Evaluate the use of the stem cell treatment to treat diabetes. **(4 marks)**

....

....

....

....

....

....

1.2 Monoclonal antibodies are also being tested to treat type 1 diabetes. The antibodies would bind to an antigen called CD3 on the surface of some cells and protect healthy insulin-producing cells.

On paper, describe how these monoclonal antibodies could be produced. **(4 marks)**

Boost your grade

Make sure that you can:
- describe and evaluate the use of clones and stem cells from plants as well as animals
- evaluate the advantages and disadvantages of monoclonal antibodies.

How confident do you feel about each of these **skills**? Colour in the bars.

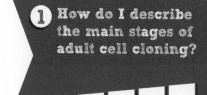

1 How do I describe the main stages of adult cell cloning?

2 How do I evaluate the use of stem cells in medicine?

3 How do I describe how monoclonal antibodies are produced?

⑦ Microorganisms and biotechnology

This unit will help you to describe and explain techniques used in microbiology and genetic engineering. It will help you to interpret the results of investigations into microbial decay.

In the exam, you will be asked to answer questions such as the one below.

Exam-style question

1 Bt cotton is a variety of cotton that has been genetically engineered to produce Bt toxin. The bacterium *Bacillus thuringiensis* produces this toxin naturally. The toxin kills insects that feed on the cotton plants.

1.1 Describe how cotton plants can be genetically engineered to produce the Bt toxin.

(4 marks)

1.2 *Bacillus thuringiensis* can be grown in the laboratory in a Petri dish on culture medium. Scientists must use aseptic technique to culture the bacterium. Define aseptic technique.

(1 mark)

1.3 Describe and explain one method of aseptic technique that scientists should use when culturing bacteria in a Petri dish.

(2 marks)

You will already have done some work on microorganisms and biotechnology. Before starting the **skills boosts**, rate your confidence in each area. Colour in 🖉 the bars.

① How do I explain the use of aseptic techniques when culturing bacteria?

② How do I calculate and explain changes in the rate of decay?

③ How do I describe the stages of genetic engineering in crop plants?

When carrying out investigations in the laboratory, contamination with unwanted microorganisms must be prevented. Pure cultures are needed when investigating one type of microorganism. Harmful microorganisms can contaminate equipment and must not be allowed to grow.

(1) Write 🖉 each key word in the box next to its correct definition.

inoculation   agar gel   aseptic   sterilise   nutrient broth   incubate

a The process of introducing microorganisms to a place where they will grow ....

b A technique used to prevent contamination with unwanted microorganisms ....

c To keep at a favourable temperature to promote cell division and growth ....

d To make something free from microorganisms ....

e A liquid solution in which bacteria can be grown ....

f Used to make a plate on which colonies of bacteria can grow ....

(2) Microorganisms cause biological material to decay by feeding on it and breaking it down into simpler substances. The microorganisms gain energy from the biological material by respiration.

a Circle Ⓐ the correct words to complete the sentences.

When oxygen is present, microorganisms carry out **aerobic / anaerobic** decay. In aerobic decay, the gas produced is **carbon dioxide / methane**. When decay is anaerobic, the gas produced is **carbon dioxide / methane**.

b Other changes can be used to measure rate of decay. When milk decays, lactic acid is produced. What could be measured to calculate the rate of decay of milk? 🖉 ....

Think about how acidity can be measured.

c A rate is a change in a quantity per unit of time.

Calculate 🖉 the rate of decay if 60 cm³ of methane is produced in 3 days.

Change in quantity (volume of gas) is 60 cm³, time taken is 3 days.

rate = ... cm³/day

$$\text{rate} = \frac{\text{change in quantity}}{\text{time taken}}$$

Genetic engineering is a process that involves changing the **genome** of an organism by adding a **gene** from another organism to give a desired characteristic. Bacteria are often an important part of this process; they may provide the desired gene and provide useful **plasmids** that act as a **vector**.

(3) **a** Definitions for the bold words are given below. Write 🖉 the correct word next to its definition.

The entire genetic material of an organism.	
A small section of DNA on a chromosome that codes for a specific protein.	
Something used to insert a gene into a required cell.	
Small ring of DNA, found in bacteria in addition to the main DNA loop.	

b Label 🖉 the main single DNA loop and the DNA plasmids on the diagram of a bacterium.

1   **How do I explain the use of aseptic techniques when culturing bacteria?**

This skills boost will help you to explain why certain procedures are carried out when culturing microorganisms in laboratory investigations.

(1) Aseptic technique must prevent contamination from all sources. Fill in the gaps ✏️ to describe the possible sources of contamination. Use the words in the box.

pathogens	air	people	gravity	water

Microorganisms are found suspended in the .... in a laboratory and

.... can make them settle out onto equipment. Microorgansims can stick to

equipment, especially when handled by .... and culture media can pick up

microorganisms from the .... used to make solutions. Some contaminating

microorganisms may be .... (cause disease), so it is

important that these are killed or prevented from growing on cultures.

(2) To explain why an aseptic technique is used, first decide what source of contamination is being prevented (unwanted bacteria coming from the air, in water or already on equipment, for example), then explain how the technique stops it. An aseptic technique is shown in the diagram.

Inoculating loop used to transfer microorganisms to the culture media.

a   What source of contamination is being prevented? ✏️

....

b   Describe ✏️ the method (technique) being used.   This technique is sometimes called 'flaming'.

....

c   Explain ✏️ why it is used.

....

(3) There are other aseptic techniques that should be used. Match ✏️ each description of an aseptic technique to the correct explanation of why it is used.

Petri dishes and culture media are sterilised before use.	Stops condensation on the lid falling onto the agar and causing contamination.
The lid of the Petri dish is secured with adhesive tape but not sealed.	Kills any microorganisms already present.
The Petri dish is stored upside down.	Keeps the lid on. Prevents microorganisms in the air falling onto the agar gel.

(4) Even with good aseptic technique, some contamination can occur. In school laboratories, cultures are incubated at 25 °C as a safety precaution against pathogens. Why is this temperature used? ✏️

Temperatures must allow microorganisms to grow fast enough, but should not be close to human body temperature (37 °C).

....

....

> 2   **How do I calculate and explain changes in the rate of decay?**

You need to be able to work out rates of decay from results of investigations presented as graphs or tables. You should be able to explain why some rates of decay are faster than others. Temperature, water and availability of oxygen can all affect the rate of decay.

1. Microorganisms cause milk to decay. They produce enzymes which break down the milk and produce acids. The table shows results from an investigation into the effect of temperature on the decay of milk.

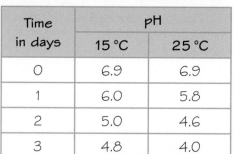

| Time | pH | |
in days	15 °C	25 °C
0	6.9	6.9
1	6.0	5.8
2	5.0	4.6
3	4.8	4.0

   a Answer the questions below to calculate the mean rate of fall in pH per day for the experiment at **15 °C** between day 1 and day 3.

   i Calculate the change in the

   quantity measured (pH):   6.0 − 4.8 =

   ii Calculate the time taken for this change: 3 − 1 = ... days

   iii rate = $\dfrac{\text{change in quantity}}{\text{time taken}}$ = [   ] pH units/day

   iv Calculate the average rate of fall in pH for the experiment

   at **25 °C** between day 1 and day 3. ....

   b On paper, explain the difference in the rate of decay at the two temperatures.

> You need to understand this investigation because it is a required practical activity.

> Decay is caused by the enzymes that the microorganisms release. So the effect of temperature on enzymes (particle collisions, optimum temperatures, denaturing) causes changes in rate of decay.

2. The diagram shows the results of a study of decay of grass cuttings. The grass loses mass because gas is given off as it decays. Two samples of grass cuttings were incubated at the same temperature. The mass was measured each day. One sample was regularly stirred (aerobic conditions). The other was not stirred (anaerobic conditions).

Answer the questions below to calculate the average rate of decay between 10 and 50 days for **aerobic** conditions.

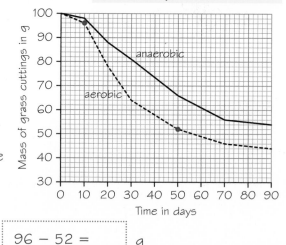

   a Calculate the change in the quantity measured. Read the values from the graph.   96 − 52 = [ ] g

   b Calculate the time taken for this change: 50 − 10 = ... days

   c rate = $\dfrac{\text{change in quantity}}{\text{time taken}}$ = [   ] g/day

> Decay is more efficient when oxygen is present; decay rate will be lower in anaerobic conditions.

   d Calculate the average rate of decay between 10 and 50 days for **anaerobic** decay.

   e On paper, explain the difference between the two rates.

3 How do I describe the stages of genetic engineering in crop plants?

To describe the stages of genetic engineering, you need to understand how a useful gene from one organism can be 'cut out' and transferred to cells of another organism.

1 The stages of the genetic engineering process are shown in the table below but not in order. Write 🖉 the letter for each stage in these sentences to describe the process.

In genetic modification, the first stage is that ☐ . The cut-out gene is then ☐ . The vector is then ☐ . The gene must be transferred to a ☐ . The new gene will be expressed in the plant, so the ☐ .

A	inserted into a vector, usually a bacterial plasmid or a virus
B	enzymes are used to cut out the gene for a desired characteristic
C	used to insert the gene into the host (plant) cells
D	crop plant will show the desired characteristic
E	plant at early stage of development, so the modified DNA will be copied as plant grows

2 a Give an example of a desired characteristic (useful feature) that might be added to a crop by genetic modification. 🖉

Use the diagram to help you.

....

b What is used to isolate the required gene from a different organism? 🖉 ....

c The isolated gene is then inserted into the vector DNA. What is the vector in this case? 🖉 ....

d Where in the plant cell is the useful gene finally inserted? 🖉 ....

e What will happen to the gene when cells divide as the plant grows? 🖉 ....

....

f What will the useful gene do in the genetically modified plant? 🖉

Genes are a section of DNA that codes for making a specific protein.

....

g Why are plants genetically modified very early in their development rather than when fully grown? 🖉

In early development, plants are made of relatively few cells.

....

....

Unit 7 Microorganisms and biotechnology   **53**

Sample response

You may be asked to calculate decay rates from a table or graph, or to describe and explain changes in rate. You might also need to explain the methods used in an investigation. This could include aseptic technique or methods of genetic engineering.

Look at this exam-style question and the answers given by a student.

Exam-style question

1 Students investigated decomposition. They placed decaying vegetable peelings into a sterilised flask. They put a carbon dioxide sensor in the flask and attached it to a data logger. They closed the flask with cotton wool. The flask was incubated at 25 °C. The rate of carbon dioxide production in parts per thousand (ppt) per day was used as a measure of the rate of decay.

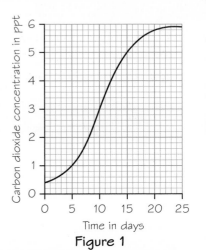

Figure 1

1.1 Explain why the concentration of carbon dioxide in the flask increased.

Because of aerobic respiration　　　(2 marks)

1.2 Calculate the rate of increase in carbon dioxide concentration in ppt per day between day 5 and day 15. Show how you worked out your answer.

0.4 ppt/day　　　(2 marks)

1.3 Why was the flask sterilised before use?

To kill microorganisms　　　(2 marks)

1.4 Why was the flask closed with cotton wool?

So oxygen from the air can still get into the flask　　　(2 marks)

Other questions may ask you to explain why decay is slower at the start of the experiment (when microorganism numbers are low) and at the end (as the food source gets used up).

① **a** The student only gained 1 mark for **1.1**. Complete the response below to gain 2 marks.

Carbon dioxide was released by .... that carry out aerobic respiration.

b The response to **1.2** is correct. Show the working for the calculation.

Show both change in quantity (ppt) and time taken.

$$rate = \frac{change\ in\ quantity}{time\ taken}$$

Sometimes you get marks for working out even if the final answer is incorrect.

c The student needed to add more detail to gain the mark for **1.3**. Write a more detailed response.

Mention where the contaminating microorganisms are and why they are a concern.

d The student's response to **1.4** explains why cotton wool was used, but not why the flask was closed. Explain why the flask needs to be closed.

Gases can pass through cotton wool but microorganisms cannot.

Your turn!

It is now time to use what you have learned to answer the exam-style question from page 49. Remember to read the question thoroughly, looking for information that may help you. Make good use of your knowledge from other areas of biology.

Read the exam-style question and answer it using the hints to guide you.

Exam-style question

1 Bt cotton is a variety of cotton that has been genetically engineered to produce Bt toxin. The bacterium *Bacillus thuringiensis* produces this toxin naturally. The toxin kills insects that feed on the cotton plants.

   1.1 Describe how cotton plants can be genetically engineered to produce the Bt toxin.   **(4 marks)**

....

....

....

....

....

....

....

....

....

Make sure you have mentioned:
- which gene is cut out and where it is taken from
- how the gene is cut out
- what is used to transfer the gene
- where the gene is transferred to
- at what stage of development of the plant this should take place.

   1.2 *Bacillus thuringiensis* can be grown in the laboratory in a Petri dish on culture medium. Scientists must use aseptic technique to culture the bacterium. Define aseptic technique.   **(1 mark)**

....

....

'Define' means 'write down the meaning of.'

   1.3 Describe and explain one method of aseptic technique that scientists should use when culturing bacteria in a Petri dish.   **(2 marks)**

'Describe' means 'write down **what** is done' (the method in this case). 'Explain' means say **why** it is done (what sort of contamination does it prevent and how).

....

....

....

....

....

....

....

Write down one thing that scientists should do to avoid contamination, then write down why this prevents contamination. Think about how contamination from air or equipment could be prevented.

Need more practice?

Questions about microorganisms, decay and genetic engineering could occur as part of a question on how microorganisms are used in agriculture or medicine or as stand-alone questions.

Have a go at these exam-style questions.

Exam-style questions

1   Beta-carotene is needed by the human body to make vitamin A. Rice does not usually produce beta-carotene. Scientists have taken the genes that enable beta-carotene production and placed them into rice. The genetically modified rice is called 'Golden Rice'. The genes for production of beta-carotene were taken from a daffodil plant.

  1.1   Describe how the beta-carotene genes were isolated from the daffodil plant.   **(1 mark)**

  ....

  1.2   The isolated genes were then placed into a bacterial plasmid. Describe how the bacterial plasmid is used in genetic modification to produce Golden Rice.   **(3 marks)**

  ....

  ....

  ....

2   Scientists studied the anaerobic decay of dry plant material to produce methane gas. The mean rate of methane production for the first five days was 20 cm³/day.

  2.1   What volume of methane was produced in the first five days?   **(1 mark)**

  ....

  Scientists repeated the experiment with moist plant material. The rate of decay was 31 cm³/day.

  2.2   Explain the difference in decay rate in dry and moist conditions.   **(2 marks)**

  ....

  ....

  ....

Boost your grade

You should be able to:
- explain how compost is produced by aerobic decay and why biogas generators use anaerobic decay
- answer questions about genetic modification of bacteria and animals as well as plants
- evaluate the risks and benefits of using genetically modified organisms.

How confident do you feel about each of these **skills**? Colour in the bars.

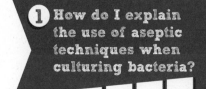
1 How do I explain the use of aseptic techniques when culturing bacteria?

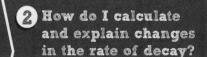
2 How do I calculate and explain changes in the rate of decay?

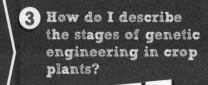
3 How do I describe the stages of genetic engineering in crop plants?

⑧ Calculations in biology

This unit will help you to show your understanding of the **quantitative units** used in biology, and how to convert between them. This will help you calculate the **real size** of very small objects. It will also help you to represent very large or very small numbers using **standard form**.

In the exam you will be asked to answer questions such as the one below.

1   A student looked at some onion cells using a light microscope.

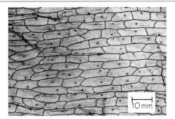

Magnification ×25

   1.1   The scale bar shows that the length of the cell in the image is 10 mm. The image has been magnified ×25 times.

   Calculate the **real size** of the cell in μm.
   Show your working.

   (2 marks)

   Real size .... μm

   1.2   Mitochondria are organelles inside the cell which release energy for respiration. A typical mitochondrion is 0.003 mm.
   Write this size in standard form.

   (2 marks)

   1.3   On average there are 3×10^3 mitochondria in a typical onion cell.

   Calculate how many mitochondria are in a sheet of onion skin containing 4×10^4 cells.
   Write your answer in standard form.

   (2 marks)

You will already have done some work on this topic. Before starting the **skills boosts**, rate your confidence in maths skills needed in biology. Colour in (✐) the bars.

❶ How do I calculate using numbers in standard form?	❷ How do I convert between units?	❸ How do I calculate the real size of very small objects?
▭▭▭▭	▭▭▭▭	▭▭▭▭

Standard form is a useful way of writing very large or very small numbers without writing lots of zeros.

7 000 000 is written as **7 × 10⁶** and **0.000 008** is written as **8 × 10⁻⁶**.

(1) Complete ✐ the table, writing the ordinary numbers from their standard form.

Standard form	Ordinary number	Standard form	Ordinary number
2 × 10⁵	200 000	6 × 10⁰	
5 × 10⁴		1 × 10⁻¹	0.1
3 × 10³		8 × 10⁻²	
4 × 10²		9 × 10⁻³	
7 × 10¹	70	4 × 10⁻⁴	

Converting units is essential when measuring very small objects that can only be seen using a microscope. The table below shows how the units relate to each other.

Learn what milli, micro and nano mean.

metre (m)	millimetre (mm)	micrometre (μm)	nanometre (nm)
1	= 0.001 m	= 0.000 001 m	= 0.000 000 001 m
= 1000 mm	1	= 0.001 mm	= 0.000 001 mm
= 1 000 000 μm	= 1000 μm	1	= 0.001 μm
= 1 000 000 000 nm	= 1 000 000 nm	= 1000 nm	1

(2) The conversion factor from m to mm is ×1000. Complete ✐ the boxes along the top in the diagram to show the other conversion factors. Fill in the correct units in the bottom boxes.

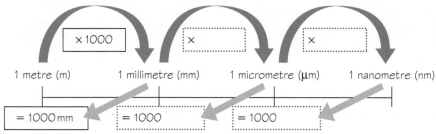

(3) Use the table to complete ✐ these sentences.

a A metre (m) is 1000 times larger than a .... (mm)

b A micrometre (μm) is 1 000 000 smaller than a .... (.................)

c A micrometre (μm) is 1000 times larger than a .... (.................)

Calculating the **real size** of a very small object requires the rearrangement of the magnification equation.

$$\text{magnification} = \frac{\text{size of image}}{\text{size of real object}}$$

(4) The image size of a cell is 50 mm. The real size is 0.05 mm. Calculate the magnification by following steps **a**, **b** and **c** below.

a Write down ✐ the image size .... and the real object size ....

b Substitute the values into the equation ✐: magnification = $\dfrac{\rule{3cm}{0.4pt}}{\rule{3cm}{0.4pt}}$

c Write down ✐ the answer: magnification = × ....

1 How do I calculate using numbers in standard form?

The method for writing numbers in standard form is shown in the diagram.

| A is between 1 and 10 | → | A | × | 10^n | ← | n (index number) is a power of 10 |

To write a large number in standard form, move the digits to the right until you have a number between 1 and 10. The number of moves is the power of 10.

$$8400 = 8.4 \times 10^3$$ (with arrows marked 1 2 3)

1. An enzyme catalyses the reaction of 980 000 substrate molecules per minute. Write this in standard form by following steps **a**, **b** and **c**.

   a Move the digits to the right until you have a number between 1 and 10. ....

   b How many moves did you make to the right? ....

   c Write the new number × $10^{(number\ of\ moves\ to\ the\ right)}$. ....

To write a small number in standard form, move the digits to the left to give a number from 1–10. The number of moves is the negative power of 10.

$$0.0032 = 3.2 \times 10^{-3}$$ (with arrows marked 3 2 1)

2. A leaf palisade cell is 0.02 mm in length. Write this in standard form by following steps **a**, **b** and **c**.

   a Move the digits to the left until you have a number between 1 and 10. ....

   b How many moves did you make to the left? ....

   c Write the new number × $10^{-(number\ of\ moves\ to\ the\ left)}$. ....

Sometimes you need to multiply numbers with powers. The diagram shows you how to do that.

$$(4 \times 10^3) \times (3 \times 10^4) = 4 \times 3 \times 10^3 \times 10^4 = 12 \times 10^7 = 1.2 \times 10^8$$

(annotations: multiply | add the powers | standard form)

3. A genetically modified bacterial cell produces 8×10^6 µg of insulin per hour. Calculate the total mass of insulin produced per hour by 3×10^5 bacterial cells.

   > Leave the numbers in standard form.

   a Write out the calculation. ....

   b Rewrite the multiplication. Group the numbers and the powers of 10. Fill in the numbers.

   > To multiply powers you add.

   > Write 24 in standard form.

   $$3 \times \square \times 10^{\square} \times 10^{\square}$$

   $$= \square \times 10^{(5 + \square)} = \square \times 10^{\square} = \square \times 10^{\square} \text{ µg of insulin per hour}$$

Here is how to divide numbers with powers.

$$\frac{(2 \times 10^6)}{(4 \times 10^2)} = 2 \div 4 \times 10^6 \times 10^2 = 0.2 \times 10^4 = 2 \times 10^3$$

(annotations: divide | subtract powers | standard form)

4. A heart contains 3×10^{12} cardiac muscle cells. The total number of mitochondria in the heart is 1.2×10^{16}. Calculate the mean number of mitochondria in each cardiac muscle cell.

   a Write out the calculation. [ ]

   > There is no need to write them as ordinary numbers first.

   b Rewrite the division. Group the numbers and the powers of 10. Fill in the numbers.

   $$\frac{1.2}{\square} \times \frac{10^{\square}}{10^{12}} = \square \times 10^{(\square - \square)} = \square \times 10^{\square} = \square \times 10^3$$

2 How do I convert between units?

When looking at cells, you need to demonstrate an understanding of the relationship between the quantitative units used to measure very small objects.

1 m = 1000 mm, and 1 mm = 1000 µm, so multiply by 1 000 000 to convert from m to µm.

① Fill in 🖉 the blank spaces on the diagram.

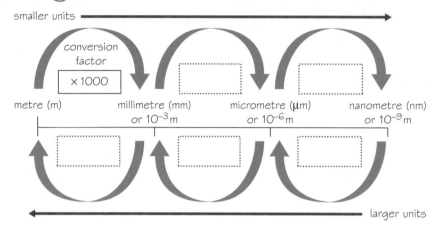

smaller units →

conversion factor
× 1000

metre (m)   millimetre (mm)   micrometre (µm)   nanometre (nm)
              or 10⁻³ m   or 10⁻⁶ m   or 10⁻⁹ m

← larger units

② A student calculates that a cheek cell under the microscope is 60 µm long. Convert this value to nanometres (nm).

- **a** Write down 🖉 the value. .... µm | 1000 nm = 1 µm |
- **b** What do you need to multiply the value by? 🖉 ....
- **c** Do the calculation and write down 🖉 the answer. .... nm
- **d** Are nanometres (nm) larger or smaller than micrometres (µm)? 🖉 ....

③ An image of a cell measures 35 mm across. Convert the measured image size from mm to nm.

- **a** Write down 🖉 the value. .... mm | 1 000 000 nm = 1 mm |
- **b** What do you need to multiply the value by? 🖉 ....
- **c** Do the calculation and write down 🖉 the answer. .... nm
- **d** Are millimetres larger or smaller than nanometres? 🖉 ....

④ A light microscope can produce a resolution of 0.001 mm. Calculate 🖉 this resolution in µm and nm.

.... µm   .... nm

⑤ Complete 🖉 the table for the different organelles.

Organelle	Size in mm	Size in µm	Size in nm
Chloroplast	0.006	6	
Mitochondrion	0.0004		
Ribosome	0.00022		
Nucleus			500 000

3 How do I calculate the real size of very small objects?

Scientists often use μm or nm to compare the sizes of microscopic objects more easily.

Real size is calculated by rearranging the magnification equation:

$$\text{magnification} = \frac{\text{size of image}}{\text{size of real object}} \qquad \text{so} \qquad \text{size of real object} = \frac{\text{size of image}}{\text{magnification}}$$

The real size will always be smaller than the image size.

1 The image size of a red blood cell is 8 mm. The magnification is ×40. Calculate the real size.

a Substitute the values into the equation and calculate the answer. 🖉

real size = ▭   real size = ... mm.

b Write 🖉 your answer to **a** in standard form.　　　It will have a negative power.

....

c What is the real size in micrometres (μm)? Tick ✓ the correct answer.

20 μm ☐   250 μm ☐   320 μm ☐   200 μm ☐

2 The image size of a root hair cell is 9×10^{-3} m. The magnification is ×40.

a Calculate 🖉 the real size in mm.　　　First convert the image size to mm.

real size = ▭   real size = ... mm.

b Now convert your answer to micrometres.　　　Multiply mm by 1000 to convert to μm
Tick ✓ the correct answer.

225 μm ☐   36 000 μm ☐   360 μm ☐   2250 μm ☐

3 An electron micrograph of a bacterial cell measures 3.6×10^{-2} m across. The magnification is ×6000. Calculate 🖉 the real size of the cell in metres (m).

▭

Tick ✓ the correct answer.　　　Convert the standard form to an ordinary number first. Divide by the magnification and write the answer in standard form.

6×10^{-6} m ☐ 6×10^{-3} m ☐ 6×10^{-9} m ☐ 3×10^{-12} ☐

4 The width of the image of a nerve cell is 5 mm under an electron microscope with a magnification of ×20 000. Calculate the actual width of the nerve cell in mm. Write 🖉 your answer in standard form.

▭　　　It will be a number between 1 and 10 with digits moved to the left so a negative power.

Unit 8 Calculations in biology　　**61**

Sample response

You may be asked to carry out several calculations based on practical work. Calculations can also be part of a theory question or use data provided on microorganisms.

Look at this exam-style question and the answers given by a student.

Exam-style question

1   *Clostridium tetani* is a bacterium that causes an illness called tetanus. Figure 1 shows some of these bacteria seen through a light microscope.

   1.1 Calculate the actual length of this bacterial cell in μm. **(2 marks)**

$$\frac{1000}{6} = 166.7 \text{ mm}$$

   1.2 *Clostridium* bacteria reproduce rapidly. The population was estimated at 4 200 000 cells.

       Write this in standard form. **(2 marks)**

42×10^5

   1.3 A patient has 8.5×10^8 *Clostridium* bacteria spread across his skin. The surface area of his body is 1.7×10^6 mm^2.

       Calculate the number of bacteria per mm^2 of skin. Write your answer in standard form. **(2 marks)**

$(1.7 \times 8.5) \times 10^8 \times 10^6 = 14.45 \times 10^{14}$

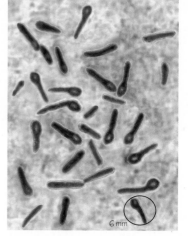

6 mm

Magnification ×1000

Figure 1

1 **a** The student did not gain any marks in **1.1**. What errors has the student made?

....

  b What should the correct answer be? ....

2 For **1.2** the student got 1 mark for the correct value but the answer is not in the correct standard form. How should the answer be written?

....

3 For the answer to **1.3**, the student multiplied the two values together instead of dividing and didn't gain any marks. What should the correct calculation look like?

The answer should be smaller than the initial values.

Remember Subtract the powers.

Your turn!

It is now time to use what you have learned to answer the exam-style question from page 57. Remember to read the question thoroughly, looking for information that may help you. Make good use of your knowledge from other areas of biology.

Read the exam-style question and answer it using the hints to guide you.

Exam-style question

1   A student looked at some onion cells using a light microscope.

1.1   The scale bar shows that the length of the cell in the image is 10 mm. The image has been magnified ×25 times.

Calculate the real size of the cell in μm.
Show your working.   **(2 marks)**

Magnification ×25

Write out the equation first then substitute in the two values.

Look back at how to convert mm to μm: 1 mm = 1000 μm.

Real size .... μm

1.2   Mitochondria are organelles inside the cell which release energy for respiration. A typical mitochondrion is 0.003 mm.

Write this size in standard form.   **(2 marks)**

Move the digits to the left until you have a number between 1 and 10. The number of moves is the negative power. 3 moves is 10^{-3}, 6 moves is 10^{-6} and so on.

1.3   On average there are 3×10^3 mitochondria in a typical onion cell.

Calculate how many mitochondria are in a sheet of onion skin containing 4×10^4 cells.
Write your answer in standard form.   **(2 marks)**

Multiply the two standard form values together but add the powers.

Do you end up with another standard form or do you need to move the digits one more time and change the power?

Need more practice?

Exam questions may ask about different parts of a topic, or parts of more than one topic. Questions about use of correct units, standard form or real size could occur as:
- part of a question on how to correctly apply these calculations
- part of a question about practical skills.

Have a go at these exam-style questions.

Exam-style questions

1 Figure 1 shows some specialised white blood cells called T helper cells. The image width of the labelled cell is 6 mm. The cells have been magnified 750 times.

Calculate the actual width of this cell in μm.

(3 marks)

Actual width .... μm

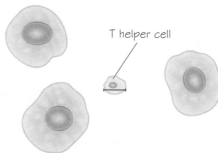

T helper cell

Figure 1

> Read the question carefully and work out what you are being asked to do. Don't be put off by the context – you don't need to know about T helper cells to answer the question.

2 A sample of the patient's blood is 5×10^3 mm³. It contains a count of 2.4×10^9 T helper cells.

Calculate the number of T helper cells per mm³ of blood.

Write the answer in standard form.

(3 marks)

Boost your grade

Practise converting between units as many biology answers require this as a final stage in the calculation.

Standard form calculations will often be to do with numbers with lots of zeros. Practise multiplying and dividing in standard form.

Microscope questions usually require magnification values but finding real size is more challenging. Practise rearranging the magnification equation.

How confident do you feel about each of these **skills**? Colour in the bars.

1 How do I calculate using numbers in standard form?

2 How do I convert between units?

3 How do I calculate the real size of very small objects?

⑨ Answering extended response questions

This unit will help you to understand what is needed for extended response questions by explaining command words so that you can work out what type of answer to give. This unit will also help you to plan and write your answers concisely.

In the exam, you will be asked to answer questions such as the one below.

Exam-style question

1   A new artificial heart is being trialled in patients with coronary heart disease.

Table 1 shows data that compares the performance of the new artificial heart design with the performance of the old artificial heart design.

Design of heart	Total number of patients in study	Patient numbers two years after the artificial hearts were implanted	
		Number of patients who are still alive	Number of patients who have died
A: New design	90	63	27
B: Old design	150	72	78

Table 1

Evaluate the data to decide which artificial heart design should be used in the future.

(6 marks)

You will already have written some answers to extended response questions. Before starting the **skills boosts**, rate your confidence in your ability to understand, plan and write with the correct amount of detail the answer to an extended answer question. Colour in (✎) the bars.

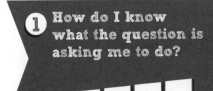

| ① How do I know what the question is asking me to do? | ② How do I plan my answer? | ③ How do I choose the right detail to answer the question concisely? |

The command word usually comes at the start of the question. It tells you what you need to do.

The exam board website lists the command words you might need to use and what they mean.

Here are some of the command words that are commonly found in extended response questions.

(1) Draw ✎ a line to link each command word with its description.

Command word	Description
Compare	Make something clear, or state the reasons for something happening.
Describe	Use evidence from the information supplied to support an answer.
Design	Use the information supplied as well as your own knowledge and understanding to consider evidence for and against.
Explain	Describe the similarities and differences between things.
Evaluate	Set out how something will be done.
Justify	Recall some facts, events or a process in an accurate way.

Exam-style question

1   *In Vitro* Fertilisation (IVF) is a process that can be used to help couples who are having difficulty conceiving a child.

Evaluate the use of IVF in treating infertility.   **(6 marks)**

(2) Circle Ⓐ the command word.

(3) What is the question asking you to do? Tick ✓ **one** box.

Planning your answer is vital because the top marks are for a sustained line of reasoning. This often means a logical order to your answer.

When you are asked to evaluate something (or two things) you should weigh up the advantages and disadvantages or risks and benefits to come to a judgement.

Describe the process of IVF ☐

Explain why couples use IVF ☐

Give the risks and benefits of IVF ☐

(4) Read these plan ideas and number ✎ them in a logical sequence. The first one has been done for you.

For an evaluate question, after an introductory sentence, there should be the positives, then the negatives and then a general conclusion.

IVF can overcome some reasons for infertility but it has risks and benefits.	1
Even though there are risks involved, I think that if IVF will help a couple they should do it.	☐
IVF can be used to overcome blocked oviducts in a woman or a low sperm count in a man.	☐
IVF does not always work first time and can take many cycles before a successful pregnancy.	☐
The embryo can be tested for genetic disorders.	☐
It can result in multiple births, which have a higher risk of miscarriage.	☐

1 **How do I know what the question is asking me to do?**

You can work out what the question is asking you by:
- looking at the command word that tells you what to do
- identifying the topic and what aspect of the topic you are being asked about
- making sense of any information given in the question.

Some questions and answers about genetic engineering are shown below.

Question

Describe the stages of genetic engineering.
Explain the effect of genetically engineered crops on biodiversity.
Compare genetic engineering with selective breeding.
Evaluate the use of genetically engineered crops in farming.

Answer content

Give the reason why genetically engineered crops may have an impact on the number of species in an area.
Weigh up the risks and benefits of genetically engineered crops.
Give a brief account of each stage of genetic engineering.
Give similarities and differences between genetic engineering and selective breeding.

1 **a** Underline Ⓐ each command word.

b Draw ✏ lines to link each question to the correct answer content.

Exam-style question

1 The bacterium *Bacillus thuringiensis* produces a toxin that is extremely poisonous to certain species of insects. The gene that produces this toxin has been introduced into tomato plants. These genetically modified (GM) tomato plants have resistance to a range of insect pests that non-GM tomato plants do not have. This means that pesticides that pollute the water and soil do not need to be applied. However, some people are concerned that eating GM tomatoes might be bad for our health. Ecologists have also warned that the toxin might affect other useful insects that feed on tomato plants.

Evaluate the risks and benefits of growing tomatoes that contain the gene for the toxin.   **(6 marks)**

2 **a** Circle Ⓐ the command word in the exam-style question above.

> The command word often appears at the start of the question.

b What is the meaning of the command word? ✏

....

c Which topic is the question testing? Tick ✓ **one** box.

genetic engineering ☐   selective breeding ☐

photosynthesis ☐   characteristics of bacteria ☐

d Look at the wording of the question and highlight ✏ the scientific information you could use in your answer.

2 How do I plan my answer?

Take a short time to plan your answer. Decide on what to include from the topic and in which order to include it.

Exam-style question

1 Stem cells are used to treat some human diseases. Table 1 gives information about using two types of stem cell to treat patients.

Stem cells from embryos	Stem cells from adult bone marrow
It costs £5000 to collect a few cells.	It costs £1000 to collect many cells.
There are ethical issues in using embryo stem cells.	Adults give permission for their own bone marrow to be collected.
The stem cells can develop into most other types of cell.	The stem cells can develop into only a few types of cell.
Each stem cell divides every 30 minutes.	Each stem cell divides every 4 hours.
There is a low chance of a patient's immune system rejecting the cells.	There is a high chance of a patient's immune system rejecting the cells.
More research is needed into the use of these stem cells.	Use of these stem cells is considered to be a safe procedure.

Table 1

Evaluate the use of embryonic and adult bone marrow stem cells for medical treatments.

(6 marks)

To gain the highest marks, your answer needs to be in a logical order. This means that the information needs to be in an order that makes sense. For example, putting all the benefits then the risks of one form of treatment followed by the benefits then risks of the other treatment.

① Organise the information you are given in the table into groups.

ⓐ Highlight ✏ the **benefits** of using **embryonic stem cells** in one colour.

ⓑ Highlight ✏ the **risks** of using **embryonic stem cells** in another colour.

ⓒ Underline Ⓐ the **benefits** of using adult **bone marrow stem cells** in one colour.

ⓓ Underline Ⓐ the **risks** of using adult **bone marrow stem cells** in another colour.

② Now plan ✏ your answer on paper, structuring your points in a logical order.

> Check that all the points have been covered.

③ Write ✏ a sentence that weighs up the risks and benefits to make a judgement.

> A judgment is a personal opinion. Make sure you support your judgement with a reason. For example, 'I consider A is a better treatment than B **because** the benefits of A outweigh the risks more than for treatment B'.

I consider that using .... stem cells is a better form of treatment because

....

....

....

....

3 How do I choose the right detail to answer the question concisely?

You can get the right amount of detail in your answer by selecting which parts of the whole topic answer this question rather than attempting to write everything you know about the topic. Refer back to the command word to work out the style and content for your answer.

Exam-style question

1 Human embryonic stem cells are used for research into certain diseases and to find out how cells respond to potential new drugs. Many people are opposed to the use of embryonic stem cells on ethical grounds. Other people feel that there are good ethical reasons for the research.

Evaluate the use of embryonic stem cells in medical research. **(6 marks)**

(1) Here are some student notes on embryonic stem cells. In each box alongside the statements write ✎ whether it is for, against or irrelevant to the argument.

Scientists in many countries are using stem cells for research.	
Embryonic stem cells are potentially very useful because they have the ability to become any type of cell.	
Human embryos deserve respect, as does any human being.	
Unwanted embryos used in stem cell research are left over from fertility clinics. If not used they would be stored or destroyed.	
The two types of stem cells are embryonic stem cells and adult stem cells that are found in adult tissues.	

Some questions will provide data in the form of a table or graph. Sometimes you will need to process the data to be able to effectively evaluate it.

When evaluating, only include information that highlights the positives and negatives that are important. General facts are irrelevant. Leave them out.

(2) Evaluate the use of two different drugs trialled to treat coronary heart disease (CHD).

Drug	Total number of patients trialled	Number of patients needing surgery in 5 years	Total cost of drug trial
A	1200	66	£120 000
B	1000	58	£112 000

The total number of patients trialled is different, which makes comparison difficult. Some processing is needed to provide useful data.

a Which drug had the highest percentage of patients needing surgery after 5 years? ✎

Drug A $= \left(\dfrac{66}{1200}\right) \times 100 =$ .... %   Drug B $= \left(\dfrac{58}{1000}\right) \times 100 =$ .... %

b Which drug works out the cheapest per patient? ✎

Drug A $= \dfrac{£120 000}{1200} =$ ....   Drug B $= \dfrac{£112 000}{1000} =$ ....

c Based on your processed data, which drug would you say is most effective in your conclusion? ✎

....

....

....

In this case, consider effectiveness and price, and refer to it in your judgement.

Sample response

Use this student response to improve your understanding. Consider what the graph is showing and use your knowledge to try to identify the issues involved. Think about what the question is asking and the science behind the data.

1 Figure 1 shows the relationship between body mass index (BMI) and the risk of developing type 2 diabetes for men and women.

Evaluate the link between BMI level and the risk of developing type 2 diabetes in men and women using evidence from the graph. **(6 marks)**

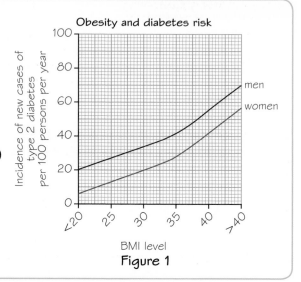

Obesity and diabetes risk

Figure 1

Here is one student's response to the exam-style question above.

At greater than 40 BMI, there were 58 new cases per 1000 women per year. As the BMI goes up the number of cases of type 2 diabetes also goes up. BMI means Body Mass Index and over 30 means that a person is obese. If they are obese, then they have a bigger chance of getting type 2 diabetes. At <20 BMI, there were 20 new cases per 1000 men per year. Men have a greater risk of developing type 2 diabetes than women because the line of their graph is higher than that of women.

1 **a** Did the student successfully 'evaluate' the link? Ⓐ Yes / No

In this question the student has to compare the risk of men developing type 2 diabetes against the risk of women developing type 2 diabetes at different BMI values.

b Highlight 🖊 where the student has made links between BMI and diabetes risk.

c Cross out Ⓧ any information that is not relevant.

This is any information not used to compare men with women or form a conclusion.

d Circle Ⓐ where the student has used the data provided to support the answer.

e What other additional or relevant information could the student have included that would improve the answer? 🖊

Has the student processed useful data from the graph?

....

....

....

f Does the response have a logical sequence? 🖊 Yes / No

g On paper, write 🖊 an improved answer.

Has the student selected relevant detail?

Your turn!

It is now time to use what you have learned to answer the exam-style question from page 65. Remember to read the question thoroughly, looking for information that may help you. Make good use of your knowledge from other areas of biology.

Exam-style question

1   A new artificial heart is being trialled in patients with coronary heart disease.

The data in Table 1 compares the performance of the new artificial heart design with the performance of the old artificial heart design.

Design of heart	Total number of patients in study	Patient numbers 2 years after the artificial hearts were implanted	
		Number of patients who are still alive	Number of patients who have died
A: New design	90	63	27
B: Old design	150	72	78

Table 1

Evaluate the data to decide which artificial heart design should be used in the future.   **(6 marks)**

(1) Circle (A) the command word.

What does the command word mean? Keep that as the focus of your answer.

(2) Converting the data to percentages will enable you to make a useful comparison.

Complete (🖉) the table.

Design of heart	Total number of patients in study	Patient numbers 2 years after artificial hearts implanted	
		% of patients who are still alive	% of patients who have died
A: New design	90	$\left(\dfrac{63}{90}\right) \times 100 = $	
B: Old design	150	$\left(\dfrac{\boxed{}}{\boxed{}}\right) \times 100 = $	

(3) Number (🖉) the plan statements in the order you would use them in your answer. The first one has been done for you.

'Evaluate' so look at arguments for and against.	1	Survival rate of the new design after 2 years is 70%.	☐
Survival rate of old design after 2 years is 48%.	☐	New design tested on a smaller sample.	☐
Old design tested on a larger sample.	☐	Comparison of survival rates.	☐
Justified conclusion.	☐	Comparison of sample size.	☐

(4) Using the plan, write (🖉) your own answer to the question on paper.

Use the data to support your answer.

Need more practice?

Exam questions may ask about different parts of one topic, or parts of more than one topic. Questions about answering extended response questions could occur as:
- questions about that topic only
- part of a question on any topic you have studied, e.g. stem cells or genetic modification
- part of a question about an experiment or investigation.

On paper, have a go at this exam-style question.

Exam-style question

1 Fertility decreases with age as the ovaries stop releasing eggs.

   In Vitro Fertilisation (IVF) can be used to help women aged 50–60 years old to have a child.

   A 55-year-old woman decided to try to have a child using IVF in 2017.

   Table 1 shows the statistics for 2017 from the IVF clinic she attended.

Age range	30–39	40–49	50–59	60+
Number of IVF treatments	125	90	25	12
Average number of embryos transferred	2.1	2.7	3.1	3.7
Number of successful pregnancies	50	27	5	2

Table 1

Evaluate her decision. Use data from the table to support your answer.   (6 marks)

> The IVF process produces embryos 'in vitro' or in a test tube. The embryos are then transferred back to the woman.

> **Remember** Plan, answer to the command word and only include relevant information or processed data in a logical sequence.

> You only have a very short time to plan, but the more you practise the faster you will become.

Boost your grade

Ensure you know the meanings of all the command words used for extended response questions.

Practise making your answers relevant by picking a question from sample assessment materials and writing the four most important points about the topic.

How confident do you feel about each of these **skills**? Colour in the bars.

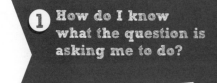

1 How do I know what the question is asking me to do?

2 How do I plan my answer?

3 How do I choose the right detail to answer the question concisely?

Answers

Unit 1

Page 2

① **a**

| carbon dioxide | ⤬ | higher concentration in alveolus than in capillary |
| oxygen | | higher concentration in capillary than in alveolus |

b carbon dioxide moves from capillary to alveolus

c oxygen moves from alveolus to capillary

② Osmosis is the diffusion of water from a dilute solution to a concentrated solution through a partially permeable membrane.

③ **a** arrow from surrounding soil into root hair cell

b arrow from surrounding soil into root hair cell

c lower; energy; against

Page 3

①

Block	Surface area (cm²)	Volume (cm³)	SA : V	Order of colour change
A	6 (= 1cm × 1cm × 6 sides)	1 (1cm × 1cm × 1cm)	6 : 1	1st
B	(2 × 2 × 6) = 24	(2 × 2 × 2) = 8	24 : 8 or 3 : 1	2nd

② **a** A 0.5; B 1

b B; concentration; greatest/steepest; fastest

③ more; faster; increase

Page 4

① out of; shrink

② solution A – lower than   solution B – equal to

solution C – higher than

③ The sprinkled sugar creates a higher solute concentration outside the strawberry cells than inside. Water molecules move from a dilute solution to a concentrated solution, so they move out of the strawberry cells into the bowl and mix with the sugar to create a syrup.

④ Arrow from cell with 15 per cent solute concentration to cell with 25 per cent solute concentration.

Arrow from cell with 25 per cent solute concentration to cell with 35 per cent solute concentration.

Arrow from cell with 15 per cent solute concentration to cell with 35 per cent solute concentration.

Arrow from cell with 15 per cent solute concentration to 25 per cent sugar solution in beaker.

Arrow from 25 per cent sugar solution in beaker to cell with 35 per cent solute concentration.

Page 5

① to the xylem cells – C
root hair cell membrane containing transport proteins – B
concentration gradient – A
low concentration of mineral ions in the soil – E
higher concentration of mineral ions in the root hair cell – D

② **a** more; lower; against; active transport; transport proteins; energy

b A – active transport   B – transport protein

C – cells supplying energy

Page 6

① **a** because they stated that excess water would affect / increase the mass of the cube

b by stating that this is because there is no net movement of water molecules

c repeat the test using concentrations between 10 and 30 g/dm³

Page 7

Exam-style question

1 Prediction: tube A will be larger / grown bigger / gained mass. **(1)**

Explanation: Water molecules will have moved into tube A by osmosis. **(1)** The water molecules will have moved from an area of (high water potential / low solute concentration) in the 5% sucrose solution to an area of (lower water potential / higher solute concentration) in the 20% sucrose solution **(1)** across a partially permeable membrane. **(1)**

Page 8

Exam-style questions

1 Waste carbon dioxide molecules move from a higher concentration inside the earthworm's cells to the surrounding air by diffusion through the skin. **(1)** Oxygen molecules move from high concentration in the surrounding air through the earthworm's skin to a lower concentration in the cells by diffusion. **(1)**

2 Pure water has zero solute concentration. The red blood cell has a high solute concentration. **(1)** The concentration gradient is very steep from pure water to red blood cell. Water molecules rapidly move into the red blood cell until the cell membrane is ruptured / damaged / lysed **(1)** by osmosis. **(1)**

3 By active transport (from an area of low mineral concentration in the soil to an area of higher mineral concentration inside the root hair cell) **(1)** using transport proteins in the cell membrane **(1)** and energy from respiration. **(1)**

4 Single-celled organisms have a large surface area to volume ratio (compared with multicellular organisms). **(1)** This allows sufficient diffusion of oxygen into the cell to meet the needs of the organism. **(1)**

Unit 2

Page 10

(1) From top to bottom: B; A; C

(2) Arrow should be downwards showing movement from air space out of stoma into air.

(3) increased air movement; increased temperature

Page 11

(1) evaporates; high; diffuses

(2) 1; 4; 2; 3

(3) It would increase the rate of transpiration because when stomata are more open, more water can diffuse out.

(4) As the temperature increases, the water particles have more energy to evaporate and diffuse therefore the rate of transpiration increases.

Page 12

(1) Arrow movement of bubble to right.

(2) (a) i 1 cm

ii 5 cm

(b) 4 cm

(c) $\frac{4}{40} = 0.1$

(3) (a) i C

ii B

iii A

(b) Straight line sketched below C.

Page 13

(1) From top to bottom: C; A; B

(2)

Area of graph	Description	Likely limiting factor
yellow	As the light intensity increases the rate of photosynthesis [increases]/ stays the same. As the concentration of carbon dioxide increases the rate of photosynthesis increases/ [stays the same].	[Light]/carbon dioxide must be the limiting factor because the graph shows that as light intensity increases, the rate of photosynthesis increases.
blue	As the light intensity increases the rate of photosynthesis increases/ [stays the same]. As the carbon dioxide increases the rate of photosynthesis [increases]/ stays the same	Light/[carbon dioxide] must be the limiting factor because the rate of photosynthesis is higher for the high CO2 concentration at the same light intensity.

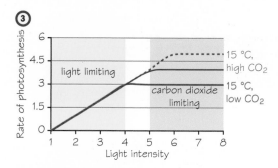

Page 14

(1) transpiration / transpiration stream

(2) **1.2**: 40 should be circled, correct answer is 25
1.4: 40 should be circled, correct answer is 25/20 = 1.25 mm per minute

(3) Increasing air movement carries away more water vapour from near the leaf surface, which maintains a high concentration gradient between the amount of water vapour inside the leaf and the amount of water vapour in the air surrounding the leaf. This increases the rate of evaporation and diffusion of water out of the stomata, therefore, increasing the rate of transpiration.

Page 15

Exam-style question

1.1 20 arbitrary units **(1)**

1.2 any one from: light intensity **(1)**, temperature, **(1)** amount of chlorophyll **(1)**

1.3 When it is hotter, water particles inside a leaf have more energy and move faster, so water evaporates and diffuses out of the leaf faster. **(2)**

Page 16

Exam-style question

1.1 4 arbitrary units **(1)**

1.2 $10.8 - 2.4 = 8.4$; **(1)** 8.4/8 = 1.05 **(1)**

1.3 Lower temperature **(1)** so slower evaporation and diffusion **(1)** / Decrease in light **(1)** could cause stomata to close so less evaporation and diffusion **(1)**

Unit 3

Page 18

(1)

Key word	Definition
allele	an allele that shows its effect when in a homozygous or heterozygous genotype
dominant allele	an allele that only shows its effect when in a homozygous genotype
recessive allele	a different version of the same gene

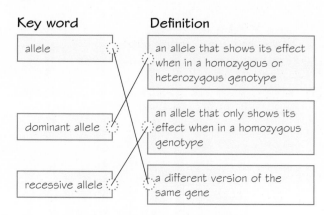

② **ⓐ** tt

ⓑ non-tongue-rolling

③ **ⓐ** Bb

ⓑ, **ⓒ**, **ⓓ**

brown-eyed heterozygous parent

		B	b
blue-eyed homozygous parent	b	Bb	bb
	b	Bb	bb

Page 19

① **ⓐ** Tt and Tt

ⓑ

	T	t
T	TT	Tt
t	Tt	tt

ⓒ 4

ⓓ TT; Tt; Tt

ⓔ 3

ⓕ 1

ⓖ tall plants to short plants 3:1

ⓗ

Phenotype	Probability		
	Fraction	Decimal	Percentage
Tall plants	$\frac{3}{4}$	0.75	75%
Short plants	$\frac{1}{4}$	0.25	25%

Page 20

① Left (from top to bottom): C; A

Right (from top to bottom): D; E; B

② **ⓑ** A chromosome is made up from a long coiled molecule of DNA.

ⓒ A gene is a section of DNA that codes for a characteristic.

ⓓ DNA is made up from repeating units called nucleotides.

ⓔ A base is part of a nucleotide.

Page 21

① **ⓐ** Sugar and phosphate

ⓑ and **ⓒ**

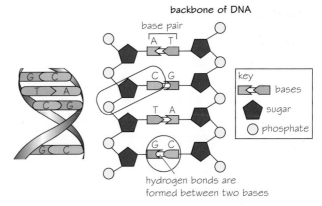

backbone of DNA

base pair

hydrogen bonds are formed between two bases

key: bases, sugar, phosphate

② G – G – T – A – A – A – T – T – A

③ CCA TTT

Page 22

① X shows a phosphate and Z shows a sugar.

② **ⓐ** They did not read the question properly. The question states to write the letter that labels the part of the DNA molecule that contains the instructions for making amino acids.

ⓑ Y

③ the order of the amino acids in the chain; which protein is formed

Page 23

Exam-style question

1.1 a homozygous recessive genotype (1)

1.2

	N	n
N	NN	Nn
n	Nn	nn

(2)

1.3 25% or 0.25 or $\frac{1}{4}$ (1)

1.4 The sequence of these bases codes for different amino acids (1) in the correct order needed to make a specific protein. (1)

Page 24

Exam-style question

1.1 5 (1)

1.2 gene (1)

1.3 C G A G G T C A G A T T G T T (1)

Unit 4

Page 26

① hormones; glands; blood; organs; oestrogen; ovulation.

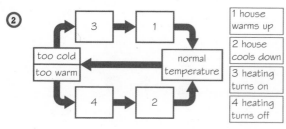

②

1	house warms up
2	house cools down
3	heating turns on
4	heating turns off

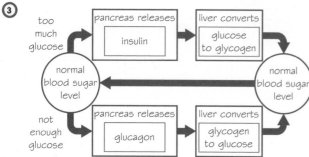

③

Page 27

① from top to bottom: FSH; progesterone; LH; oestrogen

② (left-hand column) 1, 4; 8; 10;

(right-hand column) 6; 7; 5; 2; 3

Page 28

① regulates basal metabolic rate

②

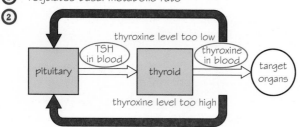

③ true; false; false

Page 29

①

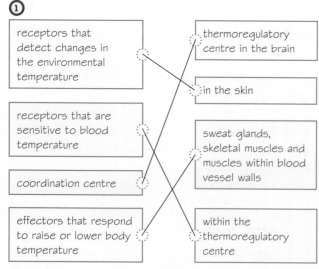

② Top box: less blood flows through capillaries; lower box: blood vessels constrict

Left-hand diagram: Vasodilation; right-hand diagram: Vasoconstriction

③ glands; evaporates; energy; environment; skeletal; respiration; released

Page 30

① **a** LH

b W = FSH

② **a** High levels of progesterone inhibit the production of LH by the pituitary gland.

b A reduction in LH levels will lead to a reduction of progesterone production. Therefore progesterone production is negatively affected by LH levels.

③ Women who have trouble conceiving have low levels of FSH and LH, so normal levels are higher.

Page 31

Exam-style question

1.1 LH **(1)** and FSH **(1)** as both rise / increase (sharply). **(1)**

1.2 A reduction in FSH levels will lead to a reduction in oestrogen production **(1)** so oestrogen production is negatively affected by high oestrogen levels. **(1)**

1.3 The thermoregulatory centre coordinates / controls body temperature. **(1)** The thermoregulatory centre contains receptors that monitor the temperature of the blood. **(1)**

Page 32

Exam-style question

1.1 Any changes in core body temperature are reversed / a rise in body temperature results in responses that cause body temperature to fall / a fall in body temperature results in responses that cause body temperature to rise **(1)** so temperature is returned back to the normal level. **(1)**

1.2 Temperature receptors send nervous impulses to the thermoregulatory centre. **(1)** Thermoregulatory centre is the control centre / coordinates the response **(1)**. Thermoregulatory centre sends impulses to the effectors (to bring about response). **(1)**

1.3 Any four points from:

Blood vessels supplying skin dilate / vasodilation of blood vessels supplying skin. **(1)** (Note: no marks for 'capillaries dilate'.)

More blood flows to skin surface / more blood flows through capillaries. **(1)**

Sweat glands produce sweat. **(1)**

Energy required to evaporate sweat. **(1)**

So more energy transferred from skin to the environment / surroundings. **(1)**

Unit 5

Page 34

① **a** one

b Fusion of gametes – Sexual

Genetically identical – Asexual

Variety in offspring – Sexual

Meiosis – Sexual

Mitosis – Asexual

c mutation

②

	Linked to
When food is in short supply, only those giraffes with longer necks survive because they can reach leaves high in trees.	Natural selection
Milk yields of dairy cows increased by 20% between 2000 and 2016.	Selective breeding
When air pollution made tree trunks black, dark peppered moths were less likely than pale peppered moths to be eaten by birds, so more dark moths survived to breed.	Natural selection
New varieties of plants with large and unusual petals are being developed by flower growers.	Selective breeding

Page 35

①

Advantage	Asexual	Sexual
only one parent needed	✓	
produces variation in the offspring		✓
if the environment changes variation gives a survival advantage, better suited varieties survive by natural selection		✓
more time and energy efficient – no need to find a mate	✓	
many identical offspring can be produced quickly to take advantage of favourable conditions	✓	

② **a** Underline: 'usually live permanently attached to rocks'

b One disadvantage of asexual reproduction is that there is no genetic variation in offspring, so if the environment changes... there would be no variation to give a survival advantage and natural selection could not happen.

c Advantage: variation; survive.

Disadvantage: slower; favourable/good; offspring.

Page 36

① **a** Underline: "species evolve, or change over time"

b Highlight: "changes that happen to an organism during its lifetime can be inherited".

c Circle: examining fossils, observing living things, experimentation.

d It backed up Darwin's ideas and provided more evidence that supported the theory of natural selection.

e Circle: supported, inherited variation, accepted.

②

The Church objected to the theory because it challenged the idea that	50 years after the theory was published.
The causes of variation and the mechanism of inheritance were not known until	there was still not enough evidence, such as certain fossils, to convince many scientists.
At the time the theory was published	God made all the animals and plants that live on Earth.

Page 37

① **a** Ticked boxes should be: B, C, D, E, F.

b Suggested highlighted words:

A There is isolation or separation of different populations.

B There are differences or changes in environmental conditions.

C There is genetic variation in the population (from mutations).

D Individuals with characteristics most suited to the environment are more likely to survive.

E These individuals reproduce more successfully.

F The alleles for these favourable characteristics are passed on to the next generation.

G Eventually new species may develop if the populations become so different that they are unable to breed successfully with each other.

② Circle: populations, fertile, species.

③ **a** Circle: different geographical areas

b Circle: climate and food type

Page 38

① Yes

② **a** Underline: Some rats might have a mutation that makes them resistant to warfarin.

b Highlight: warfarin.

c Circle: resistant to warfarin.

③ Circled words: Lamarck, wrong, cannot.

④ There is genetic variation in the bacteria and some bacteria have a mutation for antibiotic resistance. These bacteria are better able to survive the antibiotics and will reproduce more. They will pass on the allele for antibiotic resistance to the next generation.

Page 39

Exam-style question

1.1 • There is variation (in population) / mutation. **(1)**

• Individuals with longer tongues / narrow head can get more food / insects. **(1)**

- These individuals are more likely to survive / breed (more). **(1)**
- They pass on the genes / alleles / DNA (for a long tongue / narrow head). **(1)**

1.2
- (sexual reproduction) produces variation in the offspring. **(1)**
- (if the environment changes) this allows natural selection which is a survival advantage / natural selection of better suited variants allows the population to survive. **(1)**

Page 40

Exam-style question

1.1
- Populations became isolated from each other / separated on different islands. **(1)**
- Lots of different environmental conditions / different food types (between islands). **(1)**

1.2
- There was (genetic) variation / mutations in the population of seed eating finches. **(1)**
- Narrow beak was better suited to the environment / few seeds were available to eat / narrow beak was better for catching insects for food. **(1)**
- Individuals with narrower beaks were more likely to survive and reproduce / reproduce more. **(1)**
- The alleles / genes for narrow beaks were more likely to be passed on to the next generation. **(1)**

1.3
- Having similar DNA means the species are closely related / share a recent ancestor. **(1)**
- Supports the theory that all Galapagos finches evolved from the same (mainland) species. **(1)**

Unit 6

Page 42

(1) Taking cuttings of plants **C**

Adding a disease resistance gene to a cotton plant **GE**

Splitting a cow embryo into cells for embryo transplants **C**

Producing offspring by mitosis **C**

Culturing a stem cell to make lots of new cells **C**

Correcting a mutation that causes a disease **GE**

Changing a bacterium so that it will make human insulin **GE**

(2) Body cell from a child or adult, but not from an embryo

(3) divide; differentiation; marrow; meristems

(4)

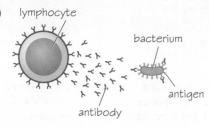

Page 43

(1)

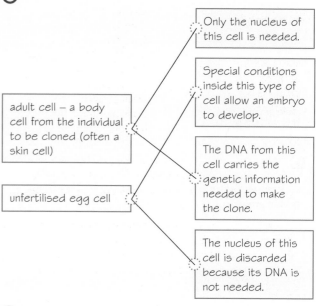

(2)

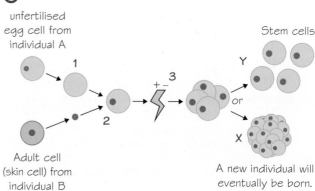

unfertilised egg cell from individual A

Adult cell (skin cell) from individual B

Stem cells

A new individual will eventually be born. This will be a clone of individual B

Page 44

(1)

Embryonic stem cells		Adult stem cells	
Replace faulty cells with healthy cells.	A	Replace faulty cells with healthy cells.	A
Can differentiate into any type of cell.	A	Will differentiate into only a few types of cell.	D
An embryo is destroyed – an ethical issue because some people believe embryos have a right to life.	D	No embryo is destroyed – fewer ethical and religious objections.	A
Stem cells can be contaminated and transfer viral infections.	D	Stem cells can be contaminated and transfer viral infections.	D

Therapeutic cloning can produce embryos with the same genes as the patient, so stem cells are not rejected by the patient's body.	A	It may be difficult to take adult stem cells from a person who is ill. The patient's body may reject stem cells from another person.	D

(2) (a) One advantage of both types of stem cell is that they can replace faulty cells with healthy cells. One disadvantage of both types is that they can transfer viral infections.

(b) Adult stem cells have the disadvantage that they can differentiate into only a few types of cell. In contrast, embryonic stem cells can be used to produce / differentiate into any type of cell.

or

Adult stem cells have the disadvantage that they may be rejected if taken from another person. In contrast, embryonic stem cells from therapeutic cloning have the same genes as the patient so will not be rejected by the patient's body.

To make embryonic stem cells, an embryo must be destroyed. This is a disadvantage because some people believe that embryos have the right to life / that destroying an embryo is the same as killing a person. However, no embryo is destroyed to make adult stem cells so there are fewer ethical objections.

(3) Overall, embryonic stem cells are a better option for replacing faulty cells because they can provide a wider variety of cells and will not be rejected if made by therapeutic cloning. However, they do raise greater ethical concerns.

Page 45

(1)

Type of cell   Description

lymphocyte ······· cell made by fusing a lymphocyte and a tumour cell

tumour cell ······· cell that divides over and over again to form a clump of cells

hybridoma ······· white blood cell that produces antibodies

(2) Answers from top to bottom: antibody; antigen; binding site; cloned; monoclonal

(3) (a) hybridoma; identical; the same

(b) Numbers as follows: 1 – by syringe; 2 – by lymphocyte; 3 – by hybridoma cell; 4 – by multiple copies of hybridoma; 5 – after final arrow

(c) Antigens / proteins from the surface of lung cancer cells

(d) The hybridoma cell can divide and so increase the numbers of antibody producing cells available.

Page 46

(1) (a) middle; unused; baby; belly

(b) nucleus; unfertilised; embryo; uterus

(2) (a) The nucleus of the egg cell from the domestic goat is removed.

(b) Arrow to show that this sentence should be at the start of the answer.

(3) The egg cell is given an electric shock to cause it to divide.

(4) The nucleus is taken from the ibex skin cell and inserted into the unfertilised egg cell. **The egg cell is given an electric shock to cause it to divide**. The egg cell will start to divide and form an ibex

Page 47

Exam-style question

1.1 Take an adult body cell / skin cell from the individual to be cloned (individual A). **(1)**

Remove the nucleus from an unfertilised egg cell (from individual B). **(1)**

Take the nucleus from the adult cell and insert it into the egg cell. **(1)**

The egg cell is given an electric shock to stimulate it to divide to form an embryo. **(1)**

1.2 Advantage: the stem cells will not be rejected **(1)** because they are genetically identical to the patient's cells. **(1)**

Disadvantage: Some people may have ethical objections to this type of stem cell **(1)** because a human embryo is destroyed to produce them. **(1)**

1.3 Lymphocyte **(1)** and tumour/cancer cell **(1)**

Page 48

Exam-style question

1.1 Possible relevant points:

Benefits	Risks
• More convenient / normal lifestyle / no need to keep monitoring blood and injecting insulin. • Blood glucose levels would be better controlled so less damage to organs. • Better to use cells from spare IVF embryo that just destroy it.	• Need to take immune supressing drugs / drugs may cause health problems • There may be risks from surgery / unknown side effects • Embryo destroyed, some people may have ethical objections / believe embryos have right to life.

3–4 marks: A detailed evaluation that considers a range of relevant points, including both risks and benefits of new treatment. Makes a conclusion consistent with the reasoning

1–2 marks: Some relevant points made but not linked together into an argument. May balance both benefits and risks. No conclusion or not consistent with the reasoning.

1.2 Any four from:

- The CD3 antigen is injected into a mouse. **(1)**
- This stimulates mouse lymphocytes to make antibodies that bind to CD3. **(1)**
- These lymphocytes are combined with a tumour cell to make a hybridoma cell. **(1)**
- Hybridoma cell is cloned to produce lots of antibody producing cells. **(1)**
- Large amounts of antibody can be collected and purified. **(1)**

Unit 7

Page 50

① **a** inoculation

b aseptic

c incubate

d sterilise

e nutrient broth

f agar gel

② **a** aerobic; carbon dioxide; methane

b change in pH

c 20 cm³/day

③ **a**

The entire genetic material of an organism.	**genome**
A small section of DNA on a chromosome that codes for a specific protein.	**gene**
Something (e.g. a plasmid or a virus) used to insert a gene into a required cell.	**vector**
Small ring of DNA, found in bacteria in addition to the main DNA loop.	**plasmid**

b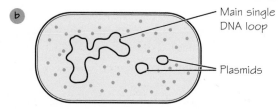

Main single DNA loop

Plasmids

Page 51

① air; gravity; people; water; pathogens

② **a** (unwanted) microorganisms on the surface of the loop

b The loop is passed through a hot / roaring Bunsen flame.

c The heat kills any microorganisms on the loop (note the loop is then cooled before transferring the desired microorganisms).

③

Petri dishes and culture media are sterilised before use.	Stops condensation on the lid falling onto the agar and causing contamination.
The lid of the Petri dish is secured with adhesive tape.	Kills any microorganisms already present.
The Petri dish is stored upside down.	Stops the lid falling off and prevents microorganisms in the air falling onto the agar gel.

④ Warm enough so that microorganisms will divide quickly, but lower than the optimum temperature for the growth of human pathogens. Incubation close to 37 °C could culture microorganisms that would make people ill.

Page 52

① **a** 1.2

b 2

c $\frac{1.2}{2} = 0.6$

d 0.9

e Decay is caused by enzymes released by microorganisms. At 25 °C, particles will have more kinetic energy. There will be more collisions between enzyme and substrate particles / more enzyme–substrate complexes will form / it is close to the optimum temperature for the decay enzymes. So the rate of decay will be faster.

② **a** 44

b 40

c 1.1

d $98 - 66 = 32$ g; rate $= \frac{32}{40} = 0.8$ g/day

e Decay is faster when oxygen is present and conditions are aerobic / there is less oxygen in the anaerobic conditions so decay is slower. Oxygen is required for aerobic respiration which is more efficient than anaerobic respiration.

Page 53

① B; A; C; E; D

② **a** resistance to insect pests / resistance to herbicide / increased yield / crops with better nutritional value

b (restriction) enzymes

c the bacterial plasmid

d into the plant DNA / chromosomes

e It will be copied into the new cells.

f produce a specific protein that brings about the desired characteristic

g It is easier to insert the modified DNA into most cells when the plant is small. Cells are copied as the plant grows so that most of the cells in the adult plant will be modified.

Page 54

① a microorganisms / bacteria

b change in quantity = 5 − 1 = 4 ppt; time taken
= 15 − 5 = 10 days

rate $= \dfrac{4}{10}$

c Sterilisation would kill any potentially harmful
microorganisms / pathogens that were already on
the equipment, so that they do not reproduce in
the flask.

d To stop potentially harmful microorganisms in the
air from falling into the flask.

Page 55

Exam-style question

1.1 Any four from:

- Gene for toxin is cut out / isolated from the
bacterium. **(1)**
- (Gene is cut out from bacterium) using enzymes. **(1)**
- Vector used (to transfer the gene to cotton). **(1)**
- Gene is inserted into cotton DNA/ chromosome. **(1)**
- Gene added at an early stage of development
(so fully developed plant cells will produce toxin). **(1)**

1.2 Aseptic technique is a method used to prevent
contamination with unwanted micro-organisms. **(1)**

1.3 Petri dishes and culture media must be sterilised/
heat treated/autoclaved before use **(1)** to kill any
microorganisms already present. **(1)** / The inoculating
loops used to transfer microorganisms to the media
should be passed through a flame before use **(1)** so
that the heat will destroy any microorganisms that
are already on the loop. **(1)** / The lid of the Petri dish
should be secured (not sealed) with adhesive tape
(1) to reduce the chance of microorganisms from the
air getting onto the culture medium. **(1)** / The Petri
dish should be stored/incubated upside down **(1)** to
reduce contamination from condensation/to reduce
contamination by bacteria settling from air in the
dish. **(1)**

(1 mark for describing a technique, 1 mark for a
matched explanation.)

Page 56

Exam-style questions

1.1 Enzymes were used (to cut out the beta-carotene
gene). **(1)**

1.2 Any three from:

- The bacterial plasmid is a vector. **(1)**
- (The modified plasmid) transfers the
beta-carotene gene to rice cells / inserts the
gene into rice cells. **(1)**
- Gene is inserted into rice DNA/chromosome. **(1)**
- (Gene is inserted) at an early stage of
development. **(1)**
- Fully developed rice plants will produce beta-
carotene. **(1)**

2.1 100 cm^3 **(1)**

2.2 Any two from:

- Survival / growth / reproduction of microorganisms is
greater when water is more readily available. **(1)**
- Microorganisms release enzymes. **(1)**
- Enzyme reactions take place in solution / water
needed to support reactions of decay. **(1)**

Unit 8

Page 58

①

Standard form	Ordinary number	Standard form	Ordinary number
2×10^5	200 000	6×10^0	6
5×10^4	**50 000**	1×10^{-1}	0.1
3×10^3	3000	8×10^{-2}	**0.08**
4×10^2	400	9×10^{-3}	**0.009**
7×10^1	70	4×10^{-4}	**0.0004**

② Top row from left to right: × 1000; × 1000

Bottom row from left to right: μm; nm

③ a millimetre b metre (m) c nanometre (nm)

④ a 50; 0.05 b $\dfrac{50 \text{ mm}}{0.05 \text{ mm}}$ c × 1000

Page 59

① a 9.8 b 5 c 9.8×10^5

② a 2 b 2 c 2×10^{-2}

③ a $3 \times 10^5 \times 8 \times 10^6$ $8 \times 10^6 \times 3 \times 10^5$

b 8; 5; 6 24; 6 24; 11 2.4; 12

④ a $\dfrac{1.2 \times 10^{16}}{3 \times 10^{12}}$

b 3; 16 0.4; 16; 12 0.4; 4 4

Page 60

① Top row from left to right: × 1000; × 1000

Bottom row from left to right: ÷ 1000; ÷ 1000;
÷ 1000

② a 60 b 1000 c 60 000 d smaller

③ a 35 b 1 000 000

c 35 000 000 d larger

④ 1; 1000

⑤ Chloroplast: 6000

Mitochondrion: 0.4; 400

Ribosome: 0.22; 220

Nucleus: 0.5; 500

Page 61

① a $\dfrac{8}{40}$; 0.2 b 2.0×10^{-1} c 200 μm

② a $\dfrac{9 \text{ mm}}{40}$; 0.225 b 225 μm

③ $\dfrac{0.036}{6000} = 0.000\ 006 = 6 \times 10^{-6}$ m

④ 2.5×10^{-4} mm

Page 62

(1) (a) Divided magnification by image size. Presented incorrect answer in mm not μm.

(b) 6 μm

(2) 4.2×10^6

(3) $\left(\dfrac{8.5 \times 10^8}{1.7 \times 10^6}\right)$

$= \left(\dfrac{8.5}{1.7}\right) \times (10^8 - 10^6)$

$= 5 \times 10^2$ bacteria per mm²

Page 63

Exam-style question

1.1 size of real object $= \dfrac{\text{size of image}}{\text{magnification}}$ so $\dfrac{10}{25}$

$= 0.4$ mm **(1)**. 1 millimetre = 1000 micrometres

so $0.4 \times 1000 = 400$ μm **(1)**

1.2 3×10^{-3} (correct number between 1 and 10 **(1)**, correct index number 10^{-3} **(1)**)

1.3 $(3 \times 4) \times (10^3 + 10^4) = 12 \times 10^7$ **(1)** $= 1.2 \times 10^8$ **(1)**

Page 64

Exam-style questions

1 $\dfrac{6}{750}$ **(1)** $= 0.008$ mm **(1)** $= 8$ μm **(1)**

2 2.4×10^9 cells/5×10^3 mm³ **(1)**

$= \left(\dfrac{2.4}{5}\right) \times (10^9 - 10^3) = 0.48 \times 10^6$ **(1)**

$= 4.8 \times 10^5$ **(1)**

Unit 9

Page 66

(1)

Compare	Make something clear, or state the reasons for something happening
Describe	Use evidence from the information supplied to support an answer
Design	Use the information supplied as well as your own knowledge and understanding to consider evidence for and against
Explain	Describe the similarities and differences between things
Evaluate	Set out how something will be done
Justify	Recall some facts, events or process in an accurate way

(2) Circle: Evaluate

(3) Give the risks and benefits of IVF

(4) 1; 6; 2; 4; 3; 5

Page 67

(1) (a) From top to bottom: Describe, Explain, Compare, Evaluate

(b)

Question	Answer content
Describe the stages of genetic engineering.	Give the reason why genetically engineered crops may have an impact on the number of species in an area
Explain the effect of genetically engineered crops on biodiversity.	Weigh up the risks and benefits of genetically engineered crops
Compare genetic engineering with selective breeding.	Give a brief account of each stage of genetic engineering
Evaluate the use of genetically engineered crops in farming.	Give similarities and differences between genetic engineering and selective breeding

(2) (a) Circle: evaluate

(b) Use the information supplied, as well as your own knowledge and understanding, to weigh up the advantages and disadvantages or risks and benefits to come to a judgement.

(c) genetic engineering

(d) genetically modified (GM) tomato plants have resistance to a range of insect pests that non-GM tomato plants do not have. This means that pesticides that pollute the water and soil do not need to be applied

Page 68

(1) (a) The stem cells can develop into most other types of cell.

Each stem cell divides every 30 minutes.

There is a low chance of a patient's immune system rejecting the cells.

(b) It costs £5000 to collect a few cells.

There are ethical issues in using embryo stem cells.

More research is needed into the use of these stem cells.

(c) It costs £1000 to collect many cells.

Adults give permission for their own bone marrow to be collected.

Use of these stem cells is considered to be a safe procedure.

(d) The stem cells can develop into only a few types of cell.

Each stem cell divides every 4 hours.

There is a high chance of a patient's immune system rejecting the cells.

② The benefits of using embryonic stem cells are they divide into other types of cells / quickly / there is no rejection.

The risks of using embryonic stem cells are they are expensive / there are ethical considerations / more research is needed.

The benefits of using bone marrow stem cells are adults give permission / it is a safe procedure / it is relatively inexpensive.

The risks of using bone marrow stems cells are there are limited types of cell / the cells divide slowly / there is a higher rejection risk.

③ embryonic/adult bone marrow

the benefits of the faster cell growth rate with low rejection rates and a greater range of cell types than with adult bone marrow stem cells, outweigh the risks more than for adult bone marrow stem cells. / The benefits of adults being able to give permission, the procedure being considered to be safe and the procedure being cheaper than using embryonic stem cells, outweigh the risks more than for embryonic stem cells.

Page 69

① From top to bottom: irrelevant; for; against; for; irrelevant

② a 5.5%; 5.8% b £100; £112

c I think that Drug A is the most effective because it is more cost effective per patient. It costs £100 per patient with a 5.5% failure rate compared with drug B which costs £112 per patient with a 5.8% failure rate.

Page 70

① a no

b As the BMI goes up the number of cases of type 2 diabetes also goes up. Men have a greater risk of developing type 2 diabetes than women because the line of their graph is higher than that of women.

c BMI means Body Mass Index and over 30 means that a person is obese.

d At greater than 40 BMI there were 58 new cases per 1000 women per year. At <20 BMI, there were 20 new cases per 1000 men per year.

e Compare the risk for men/women using the data at different BMIs. Justify the higher incidence in men at lower BMI values by using data from the graph.

f no

g *Compare the number of cases of type 2 diabetes in men with the number of cases in women at different BMIs with supporting evidence. For example: BMI<20 is 20 cases in men compared with 8 in women, which is 2.5 times higher; at BMI 30–35 it is 42 cases for men compared with 28 for women, which is 1.5 times more; at >40 BMI it is 70 cases for men compared with 58 for women, which is 1.2 times more.*

Finish the answer with a concluding sentence. For example: The risk of type 2 diabetes is

greater for both men and women at high BMI. For men the risk of type 2 diabetes is greater than for women at low BMI (<20), but the difference in the risk between men and women is much lower at high BMI (>40).

Page 71

① Circle: Evaluate

②

Design of heart	Total number of patients in study	Patient numbers 2 years after artificial hearts implanted	
		% of patients who are still alive	% of patients who died
A: New design	90	$\left(\dfrac{63}{90}\right) \times 100$ $= 70$	$\left(\dfrac{27}{90}\right) \times 100$ $= 30$
B: Old design	150	$\left(\dfrac{72}{150}\right) \times 100$ $= 48$	$\left(\dfrac{78}{150}\right) \times 100$ $= 52$

③ 1; 7; 4; 8; 6; 3; 5; 2

④ The new design was tested on a smaller sample and only 63 patients survived. The old design was tested on a larger sample and 72 patients survived. The survival success rate of the new design after 2 years is 70%. The survival success rate of the old design after 2 years is 48%. Even though the new design was tested on a smaller sample and a lower number of people survived, the actual survival rate as a percentage was much higher than that of the older design. So, the new design is the one I would choose to implement.

Page 72

Exam-style question

Sample answer:

1 IVF has made it possible for the woman to have the opportunity to have a child at 55 when it was previously not possible. This may also mean she has more time and money available to provide good parenting. The table shows that there was a 20% success rate for women in her age range at the IVF clinic she attended compared with 40% at age 30–39. However there is still the possibility of a successful pregnancy.

The downside is that having a child at 55 will mean the woman will be quite elderly when the child reaches adulthood and there are more risks associated with giving birth at 55. Information from the table shows that there is an increased risk of multiple births with increasing age. From an average of 2.1 embryos transferred at 30–39 yrs up to 3.1 embryos on average transferred at 50–59 yrs old range. So even though the treatment is less successful as a woman increases in age, there is a greater risk of having multiple births. This may not be what the woman wants.

I think that she should not have gone ahead with IVF treatment. An increased chance of an unsuccessful pregnancy would cause a great deal of stress and anxiety. If successful, the increased possibility of multiple births within her age range means there could be several children which may become very difficult to manage as she gets older.

Notes